PREHISTORIC ZOOBOOKS®
Family Activity Guide

Published by Wildlife Education, Ltd.
San Diego, California

Contents

BEE CAREFUL!

Dear Parents,

Some of the activities in this book will require your help, such as when cooking or special cutting is necessary. We have included this safety symbol on the pages where an adult's help is required.

BEE CAREFUL!
HAVE AN ADULT HELP
WITH THIS ACTIVITY

BE A DETECTIVE

Mr. Thomas had prepared food for a party. He left for a few minutes to pick up some of the guests. When he returned, someone had eaten much of the food he had planned on serving.

Use the scientific method to solve the six mysteries on this page. Examine the evidence. Find out the cause. Draw a line from each cause (who did it) to the proof. Color the picture.

2

KITTY

HAPPY

SUN

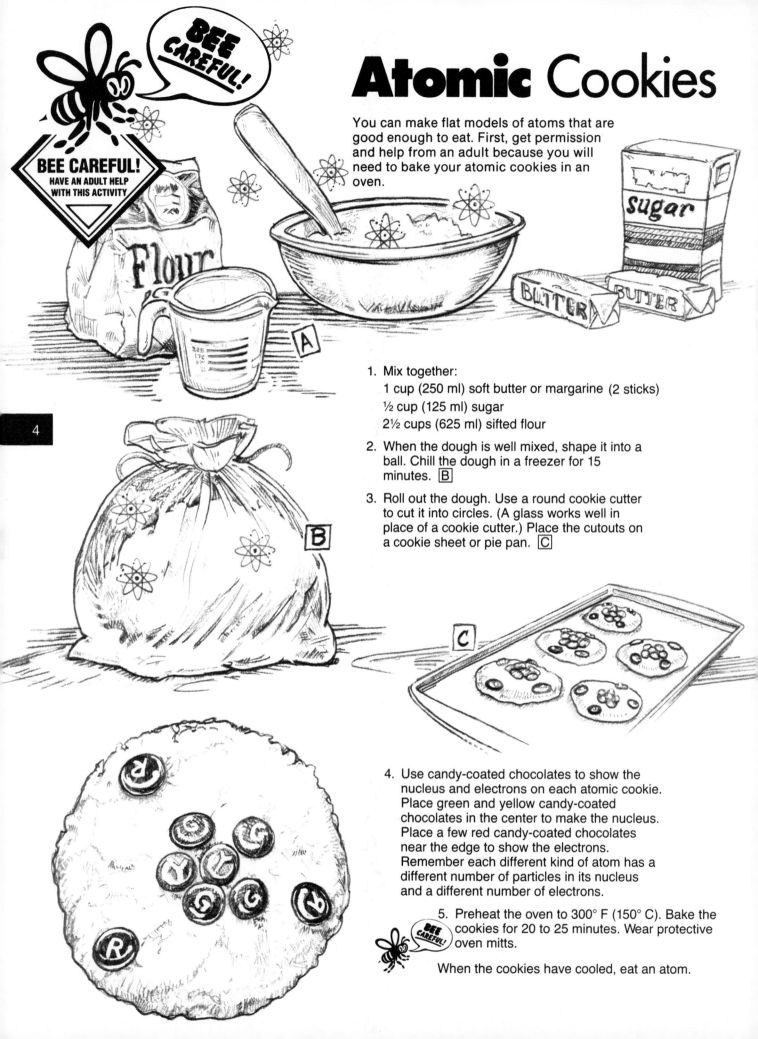

Atomic Cookies

You can make flat models of atoms that are good enough to eat. First, get permission and help from an adult because you will need to bake your atomic cookies in an oven.

1. Mix together:
   1 cup (250 ml) soft butter or margarine (2 sticks)
   ½ cup (125 ml) sugar
   2½ cups (625 ml) sifted flour

2. When the dough is well mixed, shape it into a ball. Chill the dough in a freezer for 15 minutes. B

3. Roll out the dough. Use a round cookie cutter to cut it into circles. (A glass works well in place of a cookie cutter.) Place the cutouts on a cookie sheet or pie pan. C

4. Use candy-coated chocolates to show the nucleus and electrons on each atomic cookie. Place green and yellow candy-coated chocolates in the center to make the nucleus. Place a few red candy-coated chocolates near the edge to show the electrons. Remember each different kind of atom has a different number of particles in its nucleus and a different number of electrons.

5. Preheat the oven to 300° F (150° C). Bake the cookies for 20 to 25 minutes. Wear protective oven mitts.

When the cookies have cooled, eat an atom.

BEE CAREFUL!
HAVE AN ADULT HELP WITH THIS ACTIVITY

BEE CAREFUL!

4

```
            C L D H H A Y I A
          F D Y L M Y I D I W T S T
        N E S M K T W M B M N W M F G T M
        H S C I E N T I F I C T H E O R Y T B
        B M S G T W M O T L T T M W H H J I D N R
      H N M S W M T A F G T S W M T M B I D N H V G
      H W B I F G I B H P A S B B N P A R T I C L E S T
    M M F G T W M F T O A H N W M H E S S W F A C W I A V
  B P I N T R M I H G                A W S W A E T S A M T
A I M A F A I C G                      I T A O T T I W I
H C I F T S G B E                      T I W O I F G N O
                                       E E F T O G L B S
                                       M N U C L E U S
                                       A R D I M L S G W
                                       A W F T B M T W S
                                       I H N W M B H W A
                                       T V P O F T S W H
                                       W V G A E O W F J
                                       H I A T O M S H
                                       A V O T I W T T R
```

What's the Word for...?

Several words are defined on the page.
Search for each word in the question mark.
Circle the word, then write it next to its
definition. The words go across or up and down.

```
A M O T N A P B I C P T F B V F N C T M N Y B L A D
  E B R A D Y I G I H B G A M O R I W B L W T M T D S
    F I H B V L I R T M A M D L A E M T P M B I P T G T
    I C C T B S L I A P T G T I W S W S M A D H A H N G
    I A A P G D L A T H T H N T I S D I L W H A L E X
    D E R E K H E E L E C T R O N S J E R E M Y H E
    S T E V E N I X N O N T I A P T N O A M N A N
    I T P H H O W P B E C K I S A L I N A Y O
    J A Z S A K A E J A S P P K S W R
    V H E R H I H R A
    Y Y D I T I V I B
    Q P W E R T Y M U
    Q O A S D F L E S
    A T S D F G H N K
    Z H X C V B N T M
    Q E A Z X S W E D
    C S V F R T G B N
    P I L M K O I J N
    T S D F R E C V F
    S W Q Z X C D F G
    H G F D S W R T H
    L K J G F A C D E
    S A N S A S W D F
    Q W E D F G R T Y
```

_____ An attempt to explain how something
works.

_____ A test to see if a hypothesis really explains something.

_____ Many facts and ideas gathered together
to try to explain how some part of the
world works (2 words).

_____ The very, very small pieces that everything is made of.

_____ The even smaller pieces that atoms are
made of.

_____ The group of particles that forms the
center of an atom.

_____ The particles that move around the
nucleus.

_____ Groups of atoms joined together.

```
    D K P
  L O X M E
P L M N H J K
M O L E C U L E S
  W S C F R T G
  W S R E D
  C S P
```

FOSSIL

BEE CAREFUL!

Fossils are clues to prehistory. They are traces of plants or animals that have been preserved for millions of years. You can make a fossil mold, then cast your fossil impression—in just a few hours.

If you have one, use a small shell for your fossil. A chicken thigh bone or other small, hard object will work, too. You can make more than one fossil at a time. And fossils are fun to make with a friend.

Because your fossil mold and cast must bake in the oven, get permission and help from an adult for this project.

FOSSIL MOLD

This fossil mold is made of dough. To make it, you'll need: *whole wheat flour, water, a mixing bowl, a tablespoon, baking dish, cooking oil, protective oven mitts, white glue, a small brush, and a serrated knife.*

1. For one mold, put one cup (200 g) of flour in a bowl. Mix in four tablespoons of water. If the dough is crumbly, add a few drops of water. If it's sticky, sprinkle in a little more flour.

2. Shape the dough into a ball. Work it back and forth in your hands. Squeeze and press it for 5 min-

utes. Use flour on your hands if the dough sticks. Work the dough until it is very smooth. Shape it into a ball and set it aside.

3. Spread a few drops of cooking oil in the bottom of a metal baking dish. Put the dough ball into the center of the dish and press it flat until the dough is just less than an inch (2.5 cm) thick. (Your dough should be thicker and wider than your fossil shell.)

4. Preheat the oven to 200°F (424° C). Coat your shell with oil. Press it into the dough. The shell's edges should be just below the top of the dough.

5. Wear protective oven mitts. Put the dish in the oven and bake the dough 3 hours.

6. Wear protective oven mitts. Remove the dish, let it cool, then take the shell out of the dough. Put the dough back in the oven to bake another hour.

7. Cut the dough into a square. Brush another coat of white glue over the dough. Let it dry as you begin making the cast.

CAST

To make a cast, you'll need: *thick paper, rubber band, tape, plaster of paris (or spackle paste), water, protective oven mitts, and fine sandpaper.*

 What did one paleontologist say to the other?

8. Cut a strip of paper long enough to go around the four sides of your dough mold. (It should overlap.) cut it wide enough to sit about 2 inches (5 cm) above the surface of your mold.

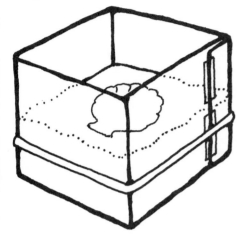

9. Wrap the paper around the mold and use a rubber band to hold it. Be sure the paper is snug against the dough. Tape the paper at the seam. Tape across the bottom of the mold in several places. Place it back in the baking dish.

10. Mix enough plaster of paris with water to fill your paper cast. As you pour the mixture into the cast, slowly fill the hole made by your shell, then fill the rest of the cast almost to the top. Lightly tap the sides of the cast several times to remove air bubbles.

11. Put the dish back into the oven. (Oven temperature should be no more than 200°F or 424°C.) Bake the cast for an hour. Wear protective oven mitts. Remove it and let it cool completely. Remove the rubber band and paper. Then carefully pull the dough and plaster apart. **There's your fossil!**

Hey! Dig this.

BEE CAREFUL!

Q **What kind of music do fossils listen to?**

A HARD ROCK

A GOOD IMPRESSION

To finish up, use fine sandpaper to smooth the sides and bottom of your plaster cast. Be sure to turn the oven off and clean up any mess you made.

Good work!

7

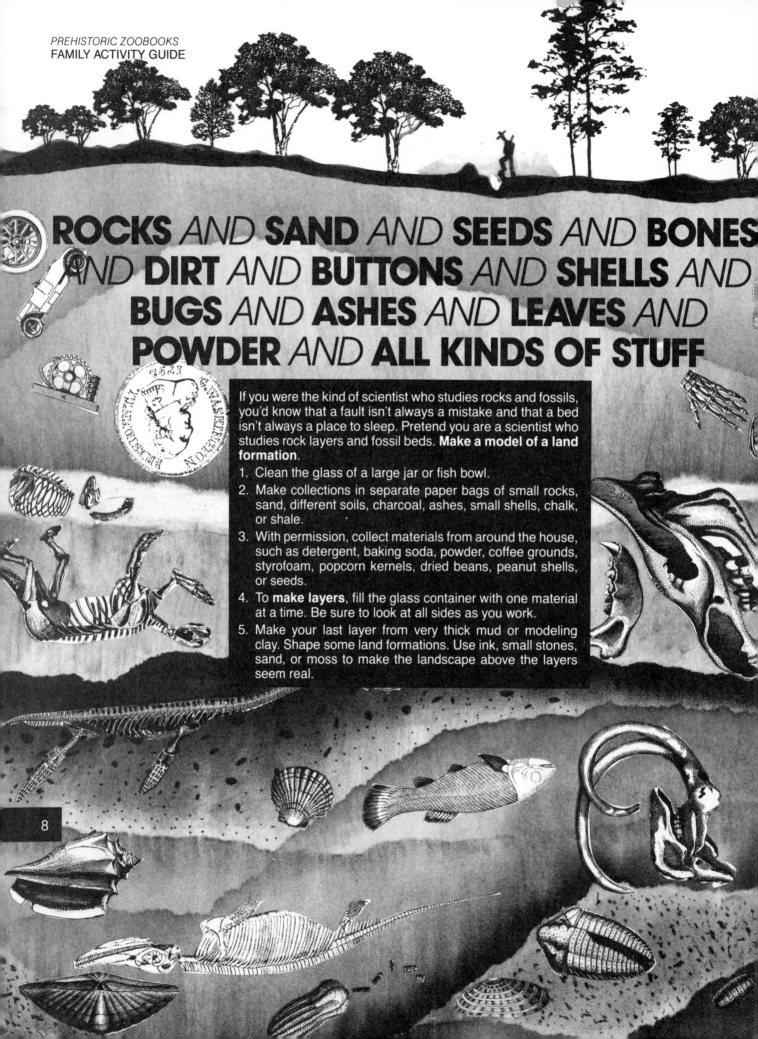

ROCKS *AND* SAND *AND* SEEDS *AND* BONES *AND* DIRT *AND* BUTTONS *AND* SHELLS *AND* BUGS *AND* ASHES *AND* LEAVES *AND* POWDER *AND* ALL KINDS OF STUFF

If you were the kind of scientist who studies rocks and fossils, you'd know that a fault isn't always a mistake and that a bed isn't always a place to sleep. Pretend you are a scientist who studies rock layers and fossil beds. **Make a model of a land formation**.

1. Clean the glass of a large jar or fish bowl.
2. Make collections in separate paper bags of small rocks, sand, different soils, charcoal, ashes, small shells, chalk, or shale.
3. With permission, collect materials from around the house, such as detergent, baking soda, powder, coffee grounds, styrofoam, popcorn kernels, dried beans, peanut shells, or seeds.
4. To **make layers**, fill the glass container with one material at a time. Be sure to look at all sides as you work.
5. Make your last layer from very thick mud or modeling clay. Shape some land formations. Use ink, small stones, sand, or moss to make the landscape above the layers seem real.

8

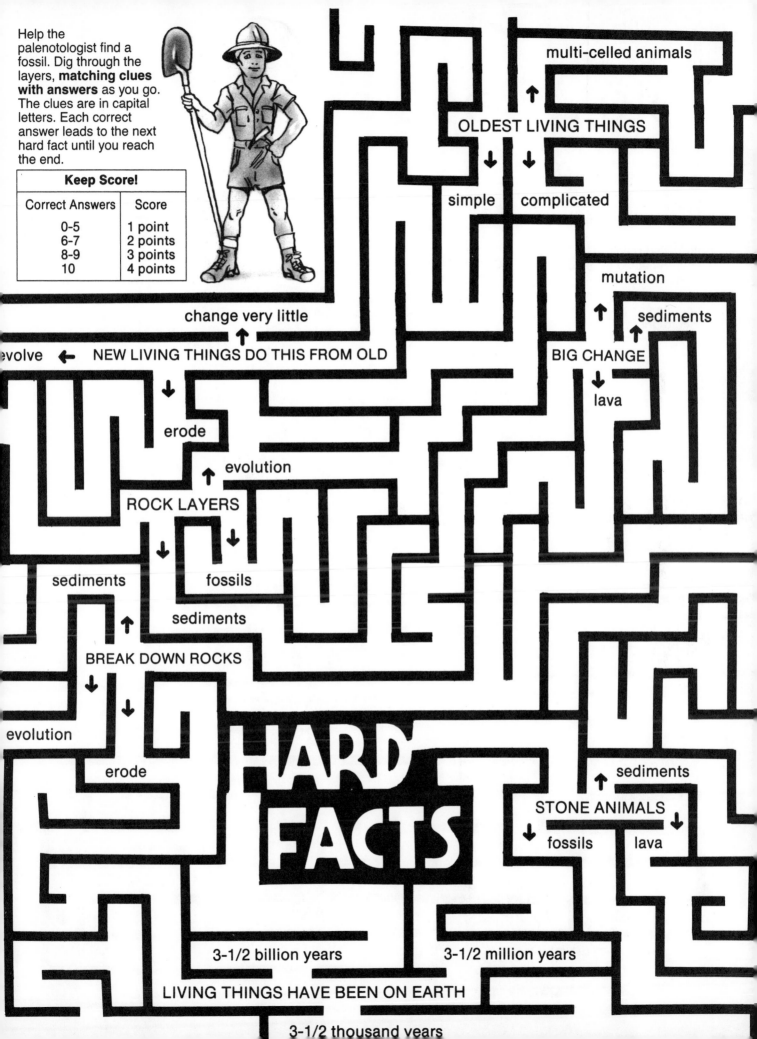

Help the palenotologist find a fossil. Dig through the layers, **matching clues with answers** as you go. The clues are in capital letters. Each correct answer leads to the next hard fact until you reach the end.

Keep Score!

Correct Answers	Score
0-5	1 point
6-7	2 points
8-9	3 points
10	4 points

multi-celled animals

OLDEST LIVING THINGS

simple   complicated

mutation

sediments

change very little

evolve ← NEW LIVING THINGS DO THIS FROM OLD   BIG CHANGE

lava

erode

evolution

ROCK LAYERS

sediments

fossils

sediments

BREAK DOWN ROCKS

evolution

erode

HARD FACTS

sediments

STONE ANIMALS

fossils   lava

3-1/2 billion years   3-1/2 million years

LIVING THINGS HAVE BEEN ON EARTH

3-1/2 thousand years

Pete AND Repeat

RepeatRepeat

The first multi-celled creatures were simple strings of one-celled plants. Pete, shown here, is a one-celled plant. Repeat is a multi-celled creature made from copies of Pete. You can make your own multi-celled creature by making **repeated prints of a simple object**. You will need: **a sponge on a dish, thick tempera paint, paper, and an object to print**.

1. Find several objects with simple shapes. You might collect a spool, an eraser, a bolt, or a small jar lid. Make practice prints with each object to decide which one to use. First, press the object against a sponge soaked in paint.

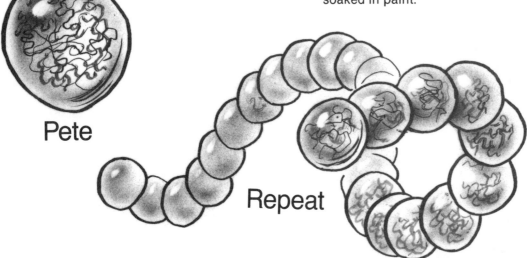

Pete

Repeat

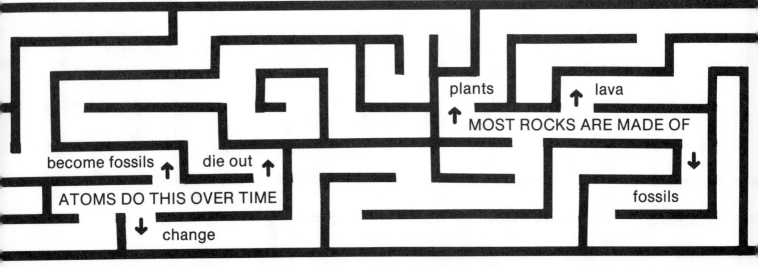

plants   ↑ lava

↑ MOST ROCKS ARE MADE OF

become fossils ↑   die out ↑

↓ fossils

ATOMS DO THIS OVER TIME

↓ change

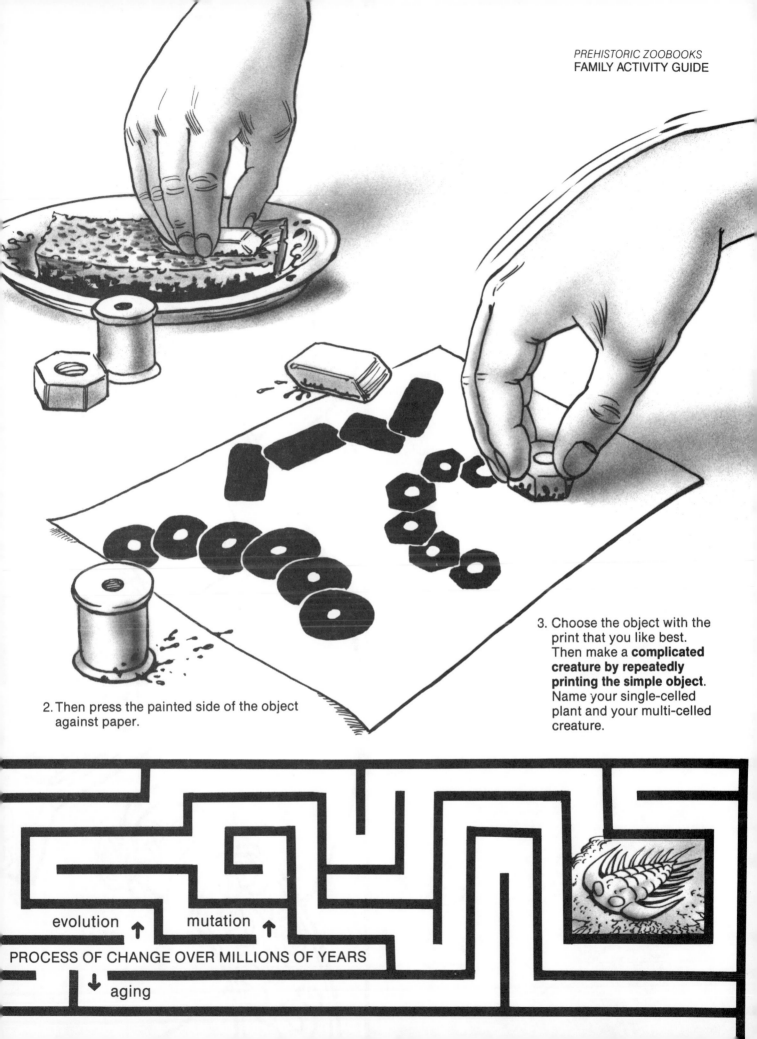

2. Then press the painted side of the object against paper.

3. Choose the object with the print that you like best. Then make a **complicated creature by repeatedly printing the simple object**. Name your single-celled plant and your multi-celled creature.

evolution ↑   mutation ↑

PROCESS OF CHANGE OVER MILLIONS OF YEARS

↓ aging

WONDERS SMALL

With a hand lens, **take a close** look at some small worlds. **Look** at patches of grass or moss. **Watch** ants around an ant hill. Look inside the petals of a flower or at algae growing on the surface of calm water. Gather all kinds of leaves, hold them toward light, and look at their veins. What else do you see? Can you see things you missed without the hand lens? Make a list of everything you look at. Make a list of everything that looks back at you!

You might start a collection of insects that you find. Some insects you might find include moths, flies, crickets, bees, beetles, or fireflies.

PHOTOSYNTHESIS

Photosynthesis is the way plants use sunlight, water, and carbon to make food for energy. The picture shows how photosynthesis would work **if a plant cell were a factory.**

In the picture, carbon atoms are shown by the letter C in a circle. Hydrogen is H. Oxygen is O. Glucose molecules, the food made by plants, are the boxes. Notice that oxygen leaves the cell (out the chimney) and goes into the atmosphere.

Color each type of atom a different color. Then color the rest of the picture.

Clayganisms

More complicated animals evolved when single cells started sticking together. Over millions of years, simple blobs of cells evolved into a wide variety of multi-celled animals. You can use modeling clay to **shape different multi-celled animals**.

3. Most sponges live in groups, or colonies, like the clay ones in ③. You can make a **colony of sponges** by repeating steps 1 and 2 several times with more clay. Then put the sponges together to make your own sponge town.

③

1. Cover your work area with paper towels. Roll some clay into a ball. Imagine that the clay ball is made up of many cells. It is like a **simple blob of cells.** See ①.

①

2. Now, you can change your simple blob of cells. Poke your thumb into the center of your clay ball. Gently pinch the sides to make a bowl. See ②. Now you have made an organism with an inside and an outside—like a **sponge** (the kind that lives in the ocean, not in your bathtub).

②

4. Now change your single sponge by making it longer. With more clay, roll out 6 or 7 thin strips to form tentacles. Attach the tentacles to one end of your changing organism. At the other end, make a lip by pinching the clay around the edges. See ④. You now have a **hydroid** with tentacles that help catch food.

④

14

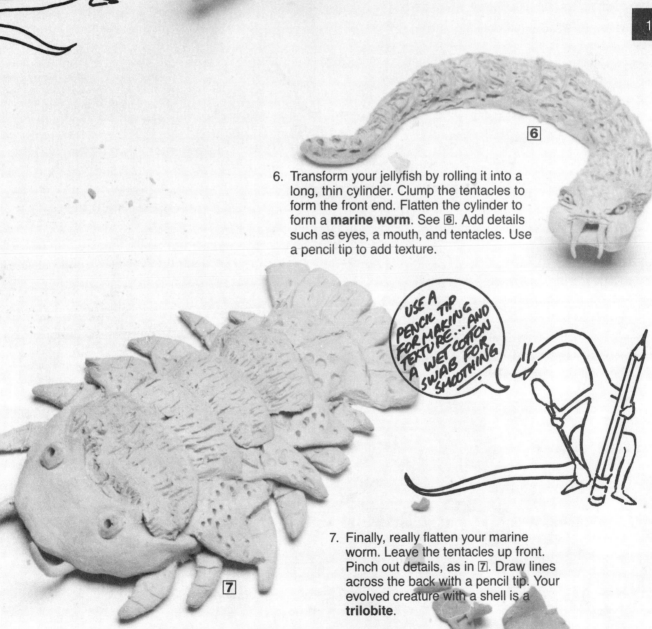

For long thin parts pack your clay over a stick or stiff wire armature.

5. Now turn your hydroid upside down. Pinch together the open end to close it. Make the end as round as possible. Pinch up a mantle around the tentacle bases. See ⑤. You have just made a **jellyfish**.

6. Transform your jellyfish by rolling it into a long, thin cylinder. Clump the tentacles to form the front end. Flatten the cylinder to form a **marine worm**. See ⑥. Add details such as eyes, a mouth, and tentacles. Use a pencil tip to add texture.

Use a pencil tip for making texture... and a wet cotton swab for smoothing.

7. Finally, really flatten your marine worm. Leave the tentacles up front. Pinch out details, as in ⑦. Draw lines across the back with a pencil tip. Your evolved creature with a shell is a **trilobite**.

Papier-mâché Trilobite

In French, papier-mâché (pay-per muh-shay) means chewed paper. It's an old craft and easy—strips of torn paper are dipped in paste and built up in layers to make a shape. You can make a trilobite model this way, and you don't have to chew any paper!

Trilobites lived in the seas of the Cambrian era. They are extinct, but many fossils of them have been found. From the fossils, we know that they had big hard shells in sections.

To make your trilobite, you will need:

A coathanger, string, several sheets of thin cardboard, liquid starch or thin water-based paste (see recipe below), masking tape, newspaper, a bowl or shallow pan, and paints.

EASY PASTE RECIPE:
Mix together one cup (240 ml) of flour and two cups (480 ml) of water. Stir until very smooth.

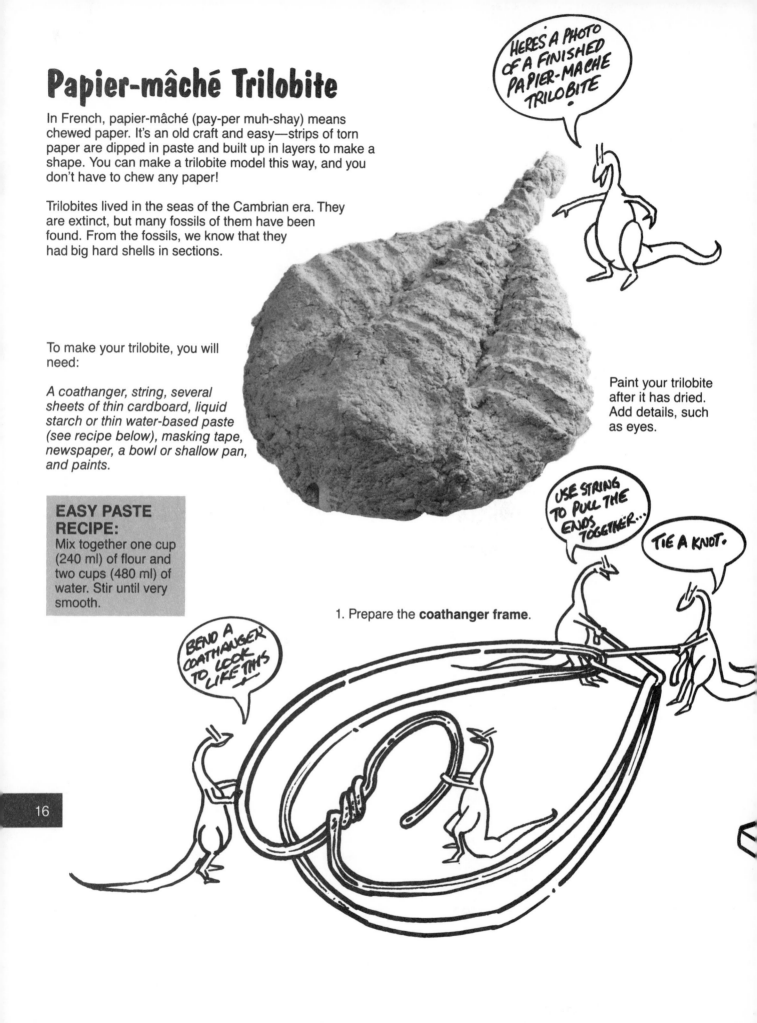

Paint your trilobite after it has dried. Add details, such as eyes.

1. Prepare the **coathanger frame**.

2. Cut out two circles from thin cardboard. Make one circle 8 inches across (20 cm) and the other 12 inches across (30 cm). Set aside the larger circle. Fold the smaller circle in half, then in half again, and in half a third time. Cut on the lines to make eight pie shapes. Use three of the pie shapes to make three half-cones.

3. Place two of the half-cones on the coathanger frame at the tail end. Tape them to the frame. Then place the third half-cone between the other two. Tape it to the outside half-cones.

4. Cut the remaining circle in half. Then cut one of the halves into three pie shapes. Cut 2 inches (5 cm) off the tip of each pie shape. Use these three pieces to form the front end of the trilobite, covering the hanger hook. Tape these pieces to the frame and to each other. Wrap the entire trilobite with masking tape.

6. Place the strip over the cardboard frame. Add strips in the same direction and overlap each strip slightly. Smooth the strips with your fingers. Once the frame is covered, begin a new layer. Place strips in the opposite direction.

5. Place the starch or paste in a bowl. Dip a newspaper strip into the liquid. Working over the bowl, slip the strip between two fingers and let the excess liquid drip back into the bowl.

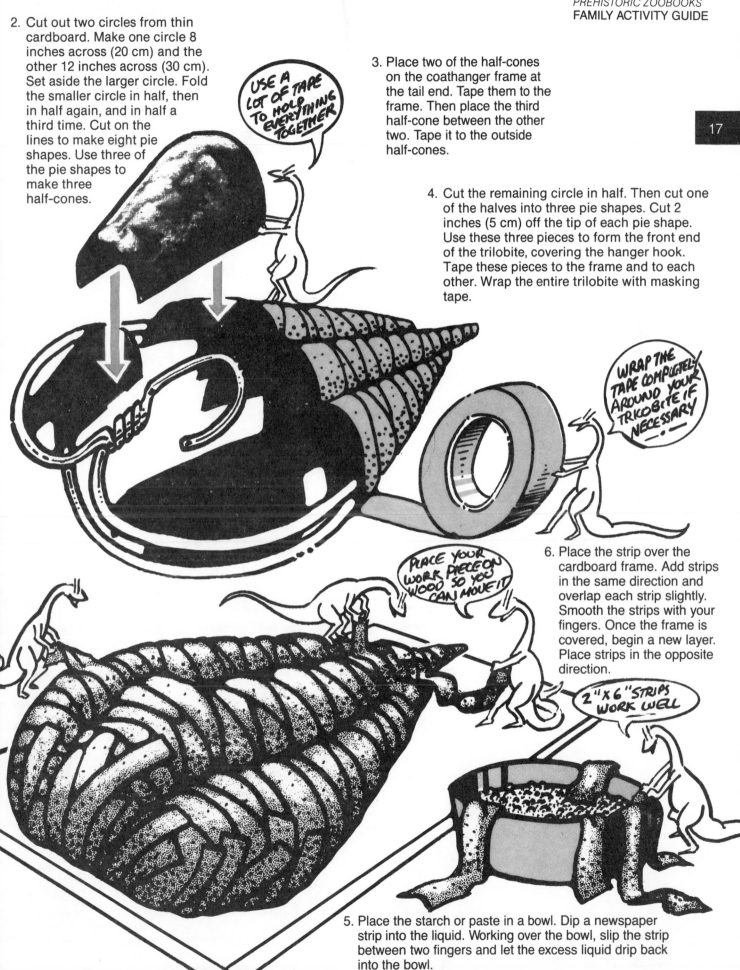

Bones!

Here's a fish skeleton you can make and mount on a stand.

1. Trace the sections shown here, **cut** them out, **paste** them to thick cardboard, and **cut** around them.

TRACE ALL THE TINTED PARTS HERE.

2. Cut the slots the same thickness as your cardboard. Then, **paint** the bones gray or white. Let the skeleton dry completely.

3. Slide the ribs into the spine. The largest rib is placed closest to the head; the smallest rib goes next to the tail.

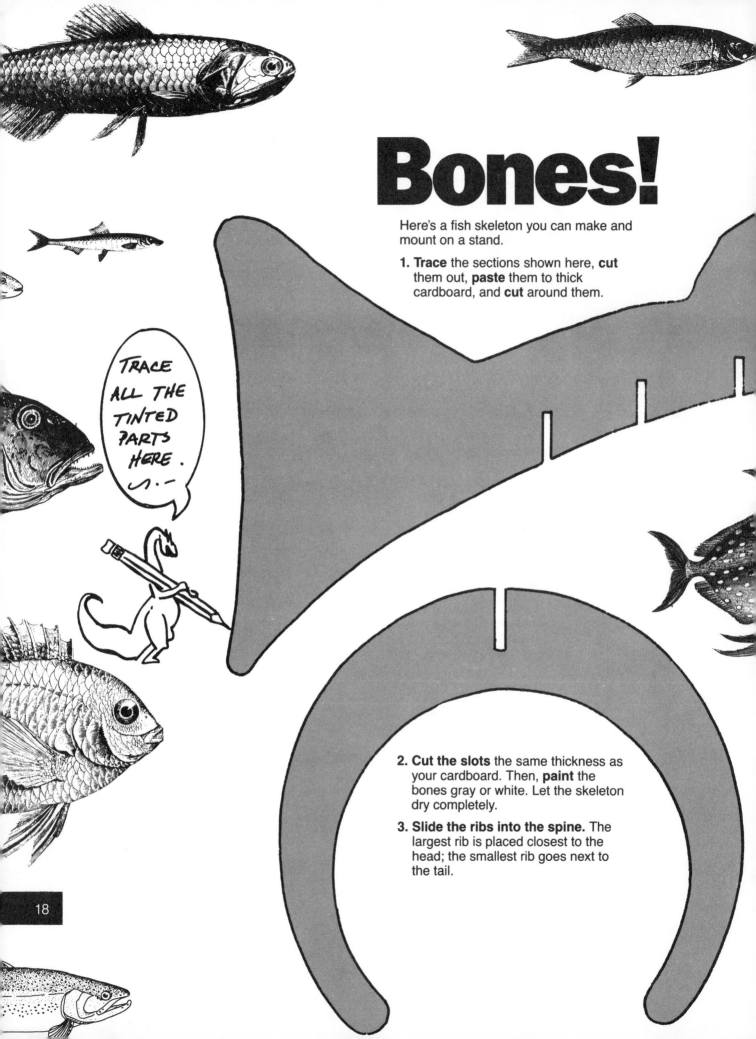

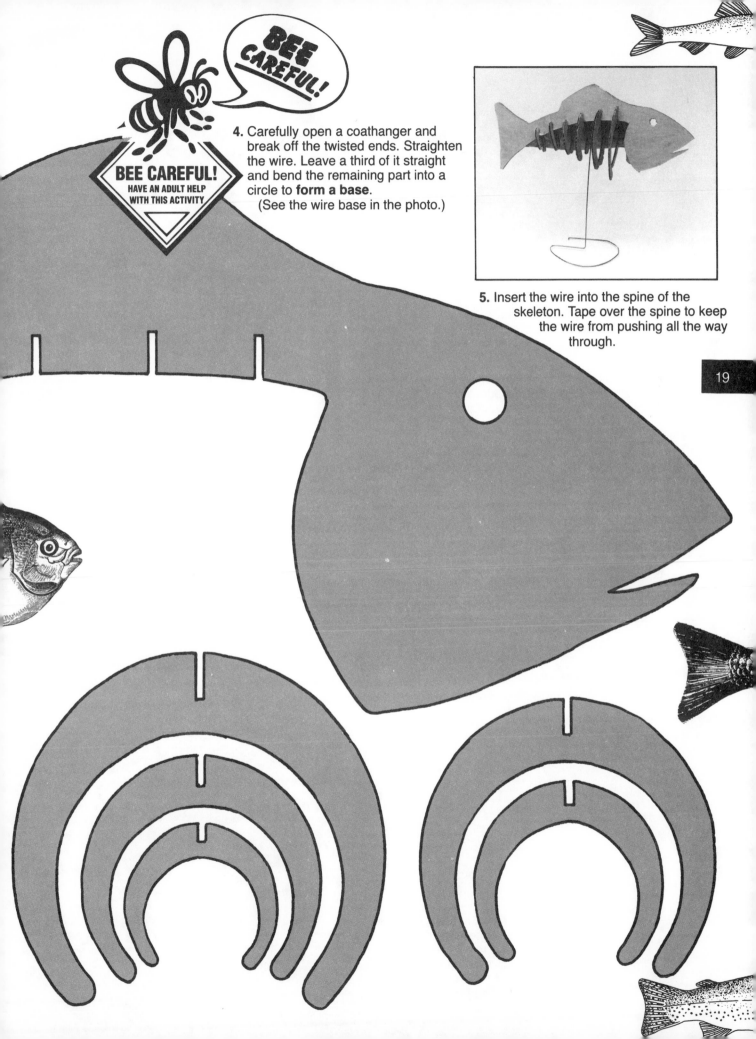

BEE CAREFUL!

BEE CAREFUL!
HAVE AN ADULT HELP
WITH THIS ACTIVITY

4. Carefully open a coathanger and break off the twisted ends. Straighten the wire. Leave a third of it straight and bend the remaining part into a circle to **form a base**.
(See the wire base in the photo.)

5. Insert the wire into the spine of the skeleton. Tape over the spine to keep the wire from pushing all the way through.

SINK YOUR TEETH INTO THIS

Sharks were probably the first animals on earth to have real teeth. You can make a model of an **ancient shark tooth** out of papier-mâché plup.

You will need: *newspaper, a bowl, liquid starch or white glue mixed with equal parts of water, an old can.*

1 Cover your work area with sheets of newspaper. Shred pieces of newspaper into small bits. Soak the bits in a bowl of liquid starch or white glue. See ①. Let stand for at least one hour. (You could start the puzzle on the next two pages while you wait.)

20

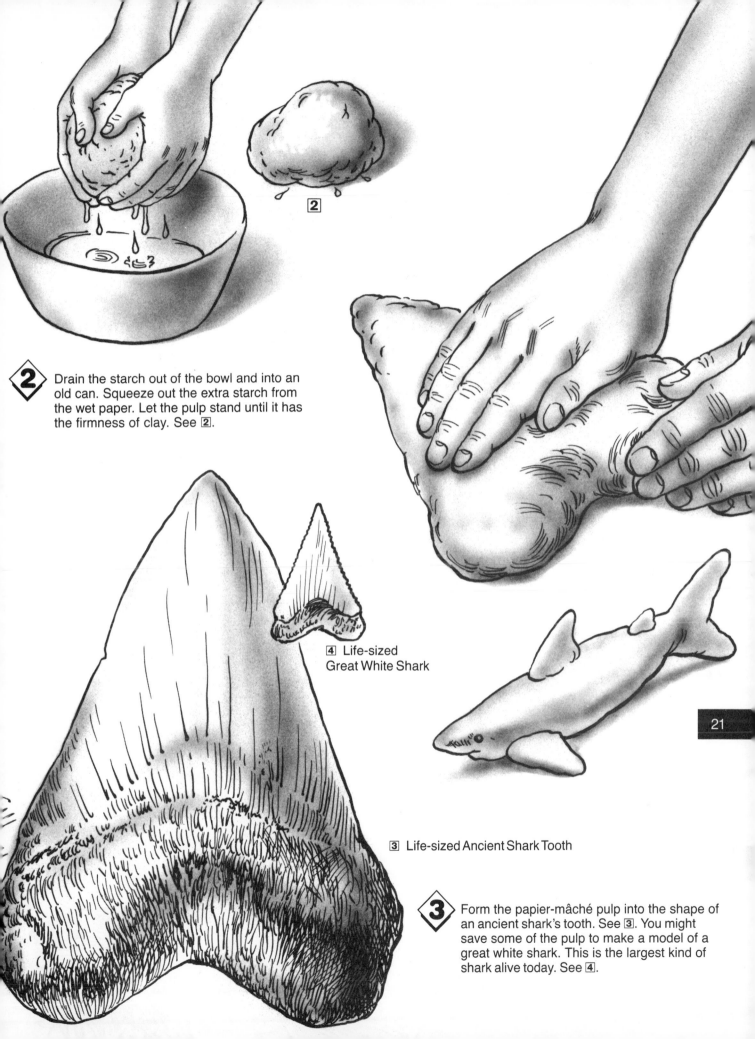

2 Drain the starch out of the bowl and into an old can. Squeeze out the extra starch from the wet paper. Let the pulp stand until it has the firmness of clay. See **2**.

4 Life-sized
Great White Shark

3 Life-sized Ancient Shark Tooth

3 Form the papier-mâché pulp into the shape of an ancient shark's tooth. See **3**. You might save some of the pulp to make a model of a great white shark. This is the largest kind of shark alive today. See **4**.

21

A FISH STORY

Something's fishy about this word search. It holds the answers to the **missing words** from the fish story. Read the story then fish for the words in the **word search.** Circle each word when you find it in the puzzle. Words go across or up and down.

Some kinds of invertebrates evolved into

_____. Tunicates had free-swim-

ming _____. The larvae of tunicates

had _____. The notochords were

_____ (two words). After a time, no-

tochords evolved into real backbones. And the larvae

evolved into _____ (two words).

Life was dangerous for the first fish. As a result, many

fish evolved hard _____ to protect

them. The armor was made of _____.

Early fish had _____

(two words), so they could only eat small food. But

some armored fish evolved _____.

With better jaws to catch more food, some armored

fish grew very big, like the giant _____.

_____ evolved streamlined bodies

with less armor. They could swim better than armored

fish. Sharks also "invented" the first real

_____. But _____

(two words) were the best swimmers. They were also

the first animals to have _____.

Bony fish also had the first _____

made of strong bone. Strong skeletons and lungs

made it possible for _____

_____ (three words) to crawl out of

the water.

```
                                    E
                                  N G E L
                                L E S T W E
                              E H I M Q W E R T Y U
                              C L D A E O E S K B E D J C D K
                              S D M S A D L O B E F I N N E D F I
                          J A W S I     M E L W J W P B I B S A D
                          I N N S K L D N E R R L K J H D G S E U K
                          D J H K H F H J N T M M N K H D F M M
                          L K J P R I M I T I V E B A C K B O N E S
                          A J F J M X V N V N I G T H H H N N V M
                            S L D P R I M I T I V E F I S H V N
                            C M V N F N J D J F J R J K E M
                              C B F G D T E D F R H F J
                                V N V B C H D H F H
                                    V N F
```

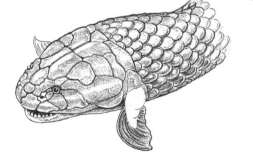

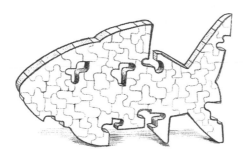

```
        I N
      V E N
   B O N E H
A O N A R
E N L I T T
A Y N G E L V
P F A S B D N G C J L S
E I L M R C S C B C W C S S B O N S D                              A L E X H E A
E S A J A S N R J W R B G T M G O J M I C N R O H W          L A R V A E
S H K D T O T B A C I A M L K U H B F L E H D S L D E D D E R M O N U E I
K E W S E A D K J F J E O R E I T U N D D A K F J H I F K D D A D K N J L
V S H J S M A L L M O U T H S L K J H F U E M N H H N N N C K H U I G A Q
N V C M N F D G J H K I L F G D K J L K J L K L L N O T O C H O R D S D S
K F H G U H V N V N K F J H G H G K J G H K H K H J              C S P D K P
D J S S D F S F D F G G G R E R R T G V F D                  Q S H A R K S
W J K L K S A D L J K U I H A M G M
S A E P F K L F M D B C N J D X
N K L E O S T E U S C K D
M F E W E F J G
E E T H C
R M O R
T A N
   S
```

What's Bugging You?

Francis the Frog is really bugged. He cannot find a single insect to eat. Can you help Francis find his food? There are fifteen flying insects fabulously hidden on this page. Score one point for every insect you find.

My score _____.

Fish Walk

   Insects were one good reason for fish to come onto land. Waters had become crowded and sometimes even dried up. Some fish had to leave the water in search of food and safety.

   This lobe-finned fish has an eye on a big lunch. But he has to get to it. Challenge a friend to a fish walk. You'll each need a marker to move through the maze and a coin to flip. Here's how to play:

   Flip a coin to see who goes first. Flip the coin to move your marker. **Heads = one square; tails = two squares.** Take turns moving your markers. If you land on a square with an insect, you get an extra turn.

   The player who reaches the arthropod lunch first wins. *Happy eating!*

Breathing Easy

We have lungs to help us breathe,
So the water we could leave.
Sun and air take wet away,
So near water we must stay.
Born with tails, hatched from eggs;
Later we develop legs.

Solve the riddle by coloring the spaces with the letters in the word **LUNGS**.

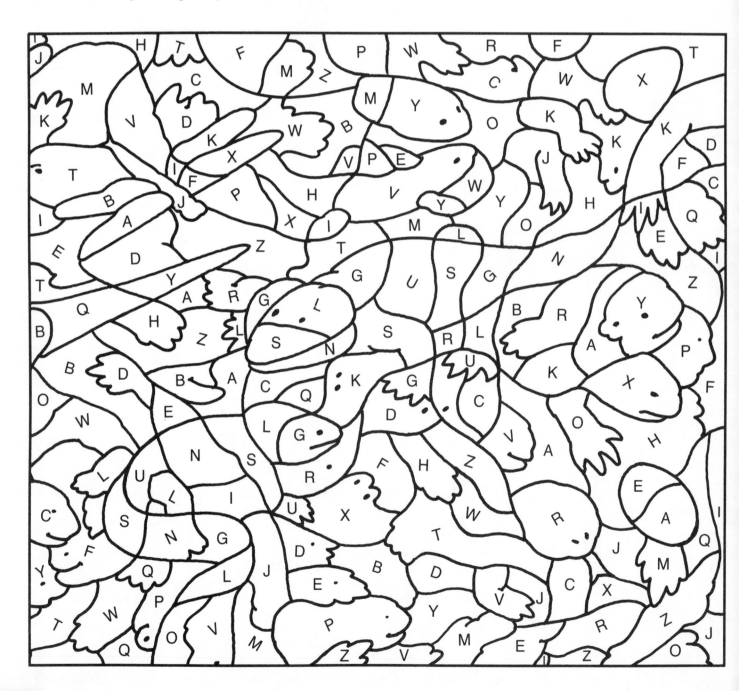

OUT-OF-WATER!

Try this crossword puzzle. Score one point for each word you complete correctly.

ACROSS

1. Hard covering of a plant that keeps moisture in.
3. Movements in water or air caused by sound.
4. Simple one-celled plants.
6. Opening in the cuticle that lets plants "breathe."
7. Group of hard-shelled animals.

DOWN

1. Material that exoskeletons are made of.
2. Hard outer shell of an arthropod.
5. Most amphibians lay these in water.

My score _____

SOLART

Reptiles cannot make heat inside their bodies. They get heat from the sun. But, if they stay in the sun too long, their bodies will get too hot. So, reptiles regulate their body heat by moving into and out of sunshine.

You can use the **sun to heat a reptile** you make. Use crayons to draw a reptile on sandpaper. Place your drawing in hot sunlight. The crayon will melt as it warms up, spreading the colors and changing the shape. But remember, reptiles cannot stay in the sun too long, nor can your artwork.

COLOR IN THE BACKGROUND LIKE THIS ONE— OR NO BACKGROUND AT ALL IF YOU WISH. THE ART AT THE BOTTOM COOKED TOO LONG!

Solart is a special kind of word. It is really two words put together—**solar** (for sun) and **art**.

COOKED TOO LONG!

EGG IT ON

The **reptile egg** was the main reason why reptiles were able to become the first real land animals. Unlike the eggs of amphibians, reptile eggs could be **laid almost anywhere on land**—and this meant that reptiles could go almost anywhere on land. The **hard shells** of the eggs kept the reptile babies **safe**. The **food** inside helped the babies grow.

You can make an artwork in celebration of the wonderful reptile egg. You can **decorate an egg** with pictures of ancient or modern reptiles. You can use felt pen, acrylic paint, fingernail polish, pictures cut from magazines, and found objects to decorate your special egg.

Ask an adult to help you follow these instructions to prepare the shells of chicken eggs that you can keep. Or, ask the adult to help you prepare hard-boiled eggs, which will only last a few days.

BEE CAREFUL!

1. Raw eggs should be at room temperature. Pierce one end of the egg with a long pin. Enlarge the hole a little with the point of the pin.

2. Pierce the other end. Make this hole larger, about ¼ inch (0.6 cm).

3. Push the clean pin inside the egg, breaking the yolk. Stir the pin. Then cover the holes with your fingers and shake the egg.

4. Hold the egg over a bowl and slowly blow through the small hole until all the egg goes out through the larger hole. Rinse the shell with warm water, then let it drain and dry. Put the "scrambled" eggs into the refrigerator. They'll still be okay to cook for a day or two.

While decorating your eggs, use masking tape for straight line designs. Pull the tape off once the paint or ink has dried. Use white glue to attach paper and other objects to the egg.

If a shell breaks as you work with it, save the pieces. You can use them to decorate other things you make, like clay beasts. Or you can collect a lot of shell pieces and make a mosaic.

Look Under?

Imagine you are an explorer looking for the world's strangest and most beautiful plant. You know it likes to live in hidden, covered places. Where would you look? What would the plant look like? Tell your story and draw or paint the plant.

Break the Code!

The codes on this page define new reptile words. Break each code to find each message. Score two points for each code you break.

 1 Start with the letter in the star. Write down every other letter. Then divide the letters into words to define **metabolize**.

TAOSBDUFRGNHFJOKOLDZAXNCDVCBHN
AMNQGWEEIRTTIYNPTAOSEDNFEGRHGKY.

 2 To define **digesting**, write down the letter in the alphabet that comes **after** each letter in the code. (In this code, A follows Z.)

GNV Z ANCX TRDR BGDLHBZK QDZBSHNMR
SN STQM ENNC HMSN DMDQFX.

 3 In the following code, all the vowels have been removed. Add the missing vowels to define **pelycosaurs**.

_ GR__P _F __RLY R_PT_L_S
TH_T GR_W L_RG_R _ND L_RG__R.

 4 Use the Morse Code to define **dimetrodon**. Morse Code uses dots (●) and dashes (▬).

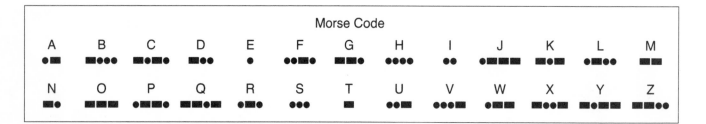

Morse Code

A	B	C	D	E	F	G	H	I	J	K	L	M
●▬	▬●●●	▬●▬●	▬●●	●	●●▬●	▬▬●	●●●●	●●	●▬▬▬	▬●▬	●▬●●	▬▬

N	O	P	Q	R	S	T	U	V	W	X	Y	Z
▬●	▬▬▬	●▬▬●	▬▬●▬	●▬●	●●●	▬	●●▬	●●●▬	●▬▬	▬●●▬	▬●▬▬	▬▬●●

 5 The letters in each of the words that define **therapsids** are backwards in this code. Rearrange the letters in each word to read the message.

PUORG FO SELITPER TAHT YAM EVAH NEEB
EHT TSRIF DEDOOLB-MRAW SLAMINA NO
HTRAE. SROTSECNA FO EHT SLAMMAM.

 6 The words that define **thecodonts** are divided every five letters, instead of where they should be. Rewrite the definition, dividing the words correctly.

THEAN CESTO RSOFT HEDIN OSAUR SHELP EDTOC
AUSET HEEXT INCTI ONOFT HETHE RAPSI DS.

 7 The definition for **nocturnal animal** is written in a number code. Use the code to rewrite the definition.

Number Code												
1	2	3	4	5	6	7	8	9	10	11	12	13
A	B	C	D	E	F	G	H	I	J	K	L	M
14	15	16	17	18	19	20	21	22	23	24	25	26
N	O	P	Q	R	S	T	U	V	W	X	Y	Z

___ ___   ___ ___ ___ ___ ___ ___   ___ ___ ___ ___   ___ ___   ___ ___ ___ ___
1 14   1 14 9 13 1 12   20 8 1 20   9 19   15 14 12 25

___ ___ ___ ___ ___ ___   ___ ___   ___ ___ ___ ___ ___   ___ ___ ___ ___ ___ ___ ___
1 3 20 9 22 5   1 20   14 9 7 8 20   19 20 1 25 9 14 7

___ ___ ___ ___ ___ ___   ___ ___ ___ ___ ___ ___   ___ ___ ___   ___ ___ ___   ___ ___
8 9 4 4 5 14   4 21 18 9 14 7   20 8 5   4 1 25   20 15

___ ___ ___ ___   ___ ___ ___ ___
11 5 5 16   19 1 6 5

My score _____

Reptiles develop eggs, so they can have babies away from water.

Move forward 2 spaces.

Egg protects reptile babies, giving them food and warmth.

Move forward 1 space.

Mammals survive and become small nocturnal animals.

Move forward 1 space.

Therapsids become extinct.

Lose 1 turn.

Dinosaurs rule the world for 160 million years.

You are the winner!

Reptiles develop skin that keeps moisture in. So, they can live in drier places.

Move forward 2 spaces.

EVOL**UTION!**

This game is for two or more players. You will need one dice or a set of numbers in a bag. (See ①.) Each player will need a small marker. Buttons and coins make good markers.

Either roll the dice or pick a number from the bag to see who goes first. The person with the highest number begins. Begin at the egg. Taking turns, roll the dice or pick a number from the bag to see how many spaces you can move forward. If you land on a square with instructions, follow them. The first person to the dinosaur wins.

① To make the numbers in a bag, cut out 6 small squares. Then write 1, 2, 3, 4, 5, 6 on one side of the squares—one number per guest. Place the numbers in a small paper sack.

It's a very cold day. Too cold for a reptile to metabolize its food.

Lose 1 turn.

Therapsids, ancestors of mammals, possibly become the first warm-blooded animals.

Take an extra turn.

Thecodonts, ancestors of dinosaurs, take over.

Move forward 2 spaces.

Therapsids develop better legs.

Move forward 1 space.

Twist and Shout

Become an expert pipe cleaner sculptor.

Make your own menagerie of prehistoric animals.

Twist a few, then listen to them shout.

Stegosaurus

1. **Twist** the ends of two pipe cleaners together. **Bend** the pair into this shape.

2. Use two more pipe cleaners to make the **bony plates.**

3. Repeat steps 1 and 2 once more. Set aside the two identical shapes until step 5.

4. Now twist both ends of two pipe cleaners together and spread the middle. This will form the Stegosaurus **tummy.**

5. Use one pipe cleaner in front and one in back to attach tummy to the bony plates you made in steps 1 to 3. Wrap excess around head and tail.

6. Twist ¾ length of two pipe cleaners together (make two pair). Bend the ends to make the **feet.**

7. Bend to this shape.

8. Position **legs** like this.

9. Wrap the structure to fill out body.

Brontosaurus

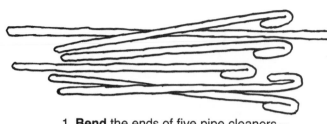

1. **Bend** the ends of five pipe cleaners— leave one more straight.

2. **Twist** one bent and one straight pipe cleaner together. Match this shape.

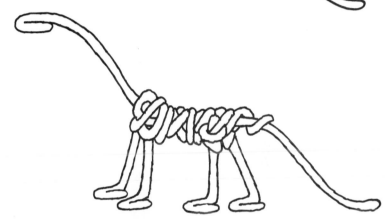

3. Twist on other bent end pipecleaners to form **legs.**

4. Wrap this stucture with pipecleaners to complete body. Make your Brontosaurus fat or thin, smart looking or silly—it's up to you.

STACKOSAURUS

B o x   U p   a   B i g   O n e

Build a prehistoric giant out of boxes. Your family or schoolmates might like to help.

1. Collect a lot of boxes, big and small. Ask an adult to help you locate a large appliance box. You'll need: *boxes, white glue, tape, scissors, rags, newspaper to keep your work area clean, and spray paint or inexpensive house paint and a large brush for the giant model. (Poster paints or acrylics work well for smaller models.)*

2. Tape the boxes closed before you stack them to help make them sturdy. Then **stack and arrange the boxes** to make your dinosaur. Use white glue to hold boxes together.

3. For a **tail**, use knotted rags to attach the boxes. Poke a hole into the facing sides of two boxes. Slip the rag through both holes. From inside each box, tie a knot in the rag.

36

Hatch a Batch
of Dinosaur Eggs Eggs Eggs

Scientists have found many dinosaur eggs. You can make a model of a dinosaur egg of your own. Ask an adult to help you complete this project. (Be sure you have permission—and don't forget to clean up any mess you make.) Here's what you'll need to get started: *potatoes (big and egg-shaped), newspaper, white glue, cooking oil, and waxed paper.*

Cut newspaper into strips about an inch (2.5 cm) wide and ten inches (25 cm) long. (One thick section is more than enough for one egg.)

Spread some newspaper over your working area. In a large bowl, mix together 1 cup (250 ml) water with ½ cup (125 ml) glue for one egg. You can add more glue and water to the mixture as you work (2 parts water with 1 part glue).

Coat your potatoes with cooking oil. Dip one newspaper strip into the glue mixture. Working over the bowl, run the strip between two fingers and let excess glue drip back into the bowl. **Wrap the strip around a potato** and pat it down. Place the next strip around the potato in the opposite direction. Cover the potato with several layers, set it aside on waxed paper to dry.

BEE CAREFUL!

Ask an adult to cut each egg in half with a sharp, serrated knife. Use a fork to remove the potato. If the potato can't be removed easily, bake the halves or microwave them until the potato softens.

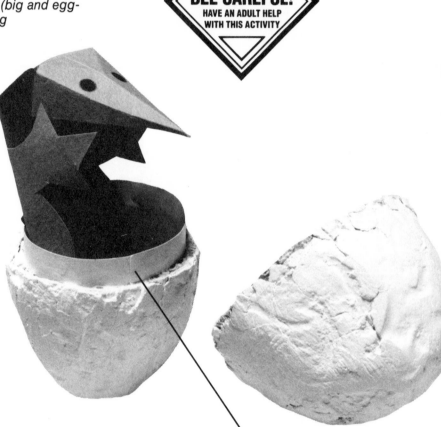

BEE CAREFUL!
HAVE AN ADULT HELP WITH THIS ACTIVITY

For each egg, cut a strip of paper about a half-inch wide (1.25 cm) and long enough, with some overlap, to fit inside the rim of one egg half. Glue the ends of the strip together where they overlap. Rub glue on the inside rim of the egg half. Insert the paper ring so that half of it sticks out of the egg half. Once the glue has dried, you can put the two egg halves together.

Paint your eggs any way you like. You could use an old toothbrush to spatter eggs for a speckled look. (Do this outside—it's messy. Practice a few times with paper before you work on your eggs.) Dip the toothbrush into paint, tap the brush to avoid big drips, then aim the brush at the egg and run a finger over the bristles. Don't work too closely to the egg. When the paint has dried, roll the egg over to spatter the other side.

It gets wet.

Here's the pattern for a baby dinosaur. Trace the pattern, cut it out, and use it to draw the outline onto stiff, colored paper. Cut out the shape from the paper. Fold it along the lines shown here.

Draw some big eyes, then put the little tyke into your egg!

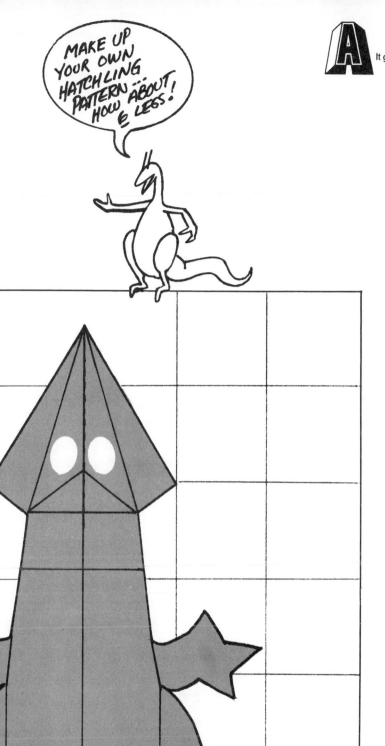

NAME THAT DINOSAUR

Dinosaurs ruled the earth for over 160 million years. In that time many different kinds of dinosaurs came and went. Some of the more popular species are shown in the picture above. How many of them can you name? Score one point for each one you correctly identify.

My score _____

DINOSAUR DIORAMA

You can create your own prehistoric world by making a **diorama**. Use a cardboard box with a lid or closable top for your ancient world. Your environment will include prehistoric animals and plants.

1. Cut a hole in one end of your box for viewing the diorama. This will be the **point of view** from which the things you put in the diorama will be seen. Also cut a hole in the top of the box to let in light. You might even want to shine a flashlight into your invented world.
2. Plan a **prehistoric environment** for the inside of your box. Plan ways to cover the walls and ceiling of your box. Cut out pictures, shapes, and colors from magazines. Paste the cutouts around the inside of the box for a background. Also, use paint or markers to create the world you've imagined.
3. You might cover the **floor** of the box with sandpaper. Use crayons to add details. Add rocks and twigs.
4. For prehistoric **plant life**, you might cut paper or cloth. Also, use ribbons, cotton balls, and sponges. You might add some parts from real plants.
5. With modeling clay, shape **dinosaurs** or other prehistoric animals. You might hang some paper animals from inside the lid.

41

?

What's big and goes slam, slam, slam, slam?

A

A four-door dinosaur.

DINOSAUR PICNIC

O ne warm day every year, the dinosaurs gave their claws, teeth, spikes, and clubtails a rest. They stopped fighting over food and stopped eating each other. They had a **dinosaur picnic**. Well, they didn't really. But *you* can.

Invite your friends. Tell them that you've discovered some incredible dinosaur tracks. And you want to celebrate and have a big picnic before the world famous paleontologist Professor Elitper comes along. Everyone should wear clothes they can get dirty. You might ask people to bring some of the foods needed for the Crunchy Osaurtment Contest.

PUTTING ON THE DINO DOG

Invite your guests to turn roasted hot dogs into dinosaurs. You and your guests can use lettuce and tomatoes to add legs, tails, and heads to the hot dogs. Squirt on details in ketchup and mustard. Corn chips, potato chips, pretzels, chopped onion, and pickles can be used, too. Then, quickly before the dino dogs disappear, ask a judge to choose a winner.

Professor Elitper's name spells something backwards!

42

A CRUNCHY OSAURTMENT

Not every treat has to be for carnivores. These fruit and vegetable treats will attract the herbivore dinosaurs among your friends. Your guests might enjoy creating Crunchy Osaurtments for a contest.

Provide celery stalks to be filled with peanut butter or cream cheese and crackers to be covered with peanut butter or cheese. Contestants can choose from the following to decorate their herbivore treats:
celery leaves • sliced almonds • raisins dried apricots • peanuts • cereal • popcorn • pretzels • carrot slices • sunflower seeds • pear slices • apple slices • other fruit slices

3 WAY RELAY

Some dinosaurs were speedy little whipper-snappers. Others lumbered along. Have a relay race that shows dinosaur movement. Have the guests form teams of three members. One person from each team will run each part of the race.

① Run with arms raised!

One person from each team will form the group that runs this part of the race. These team members will **run** with their **arms raised**. They will run to members of their own teams, who are waiting at a specific place on the race course. (The waiting runners cannot move until they are tagged by their own team members who are running with their arms raised.)

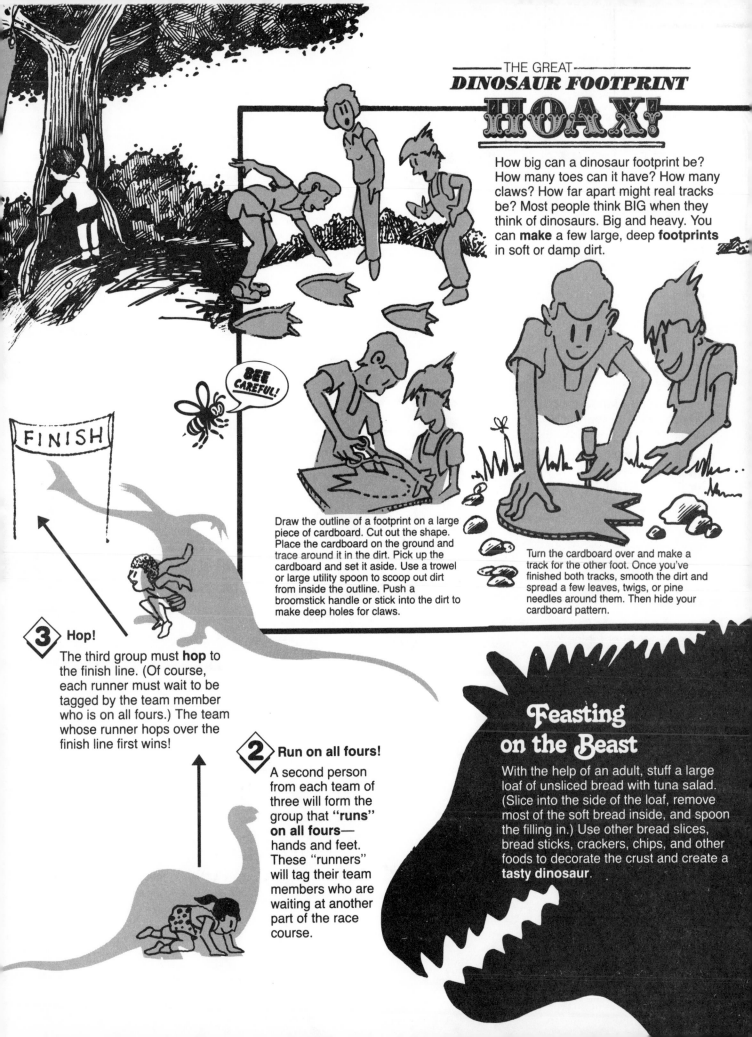

THE GREAT DINOSAUR FOOTPRINT HOAX!

How big can a dinosaur footprint be? How many toes can it have? How many claws? How far apart might real tracks be? Most people think BIG when they think of dinosaurs. Big and heavy. You can **make** a few large, deep **footprints** in soft or damp dirt.

Draw the outline of a footprint on a large piece of cardboard. Cut out the shape. Place the cardboard on the ground and trace around it in the dirt. Pick up the cardboard and set it aside. Use a trowel or large utility spoon to scoop out dirt from inside the outline. Push a broomstick handle or stick into the dirt to make deep holes for claws.

Turn the cardboard over and make a track for the other foot. Once you've finished both tracks, smooth the dirt and spread a few leaves, twigs, or pine needles around them. Then hide your cardboard pattern.

BEE CAREFUL!

FINISH

3 Hop!

The third group must **hop** to the finish line. (Of course, each runner must wait to be tagged by the team member who is on all fours.) The team whose runner hops over the finish line first wins!

2 Run on all fours!

A second person from each team of three will form the group that **"runs" on all fours**— hands and feet. These "runners" will tag their team members who are waiting at another part of the race course.

Feasting on the Beast

With the help of an adult, stuff a large loaf of unsliced bread with tuna salad. (Slice into the side of the loaf, remove most of the soft bread inside, and spoon the filling in.) Use other bread slices, bread sticks, crackers, chips, and other foods to decorate the crust and create a **tasty dinosaur**.

MIGHTY FLIGHTY

Pterosaurs were flying reptiles that lived at the time of dinosaurs. Some were small, but others had wingspans of up to 40 feet (12 m). Some had teeth and tails. Some had huge crests on the backs of their heads. Many were probably more gliders than flyers, cruising on upward air currents, like a kite.

Make a fantastic *Pterosaur* kite for a breezy day. You'll need: three thin-wire coathangers, newspaper, masking tape, white glue, a large paintbrush, string, and thick paper.

Kite Body

Ask an adult to follow these instructions to prepare the coathanger frame for you:

- Open the coathangers. Break off the hooked ends and straighten each wire. Bend the coiled ends at an angle. From the bend, measure 18 inches (45 cm) and make a second bend in each wire. (See ①.) Break the third coathanger about 2 inches (5 cm) above each of its "elbows."

- Adjust the bends you made so that the hangers lie flat. Tape the hangers together for the kite frame as shown in ①.

Begin the paper covering:

1. Mix together one cup of water (250 ml) and ½ cup of glue (125 ml). Add more glue and water as you work (two parts water with one part white glue), if needed.

2. Brush the glue mixture evenly over an unfolded sheet of newspaper. Place your wire frame on the sheet, position another sheet of newspaper on top, and pat the sheets together. Let the glue dry completely.

3. Hold the paper up to light to see the outline of the frame, then mark the kite pattern shown in ②. Cut out the pattern.

BEE CAREFUL!

BEE CAREFUL!
HAVE AN ADULT HELP
WITH THIS ACTIVITY

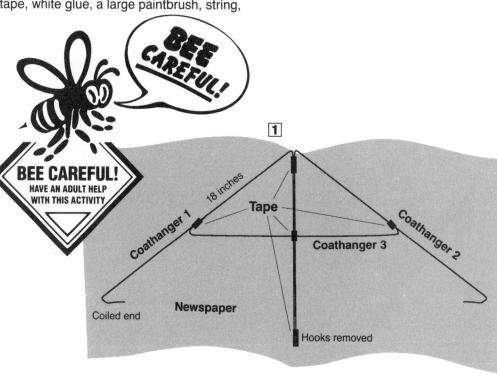

① Coathanger 1 — 18 inches — Tape — Coathanger 3 — Coathanger 2 — Coiled end — Newspaper — Hooks removed

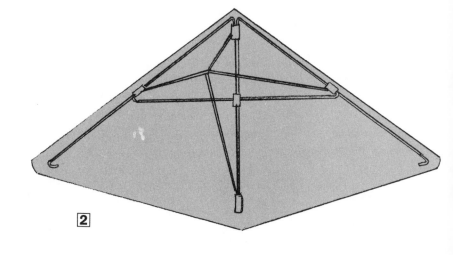

②

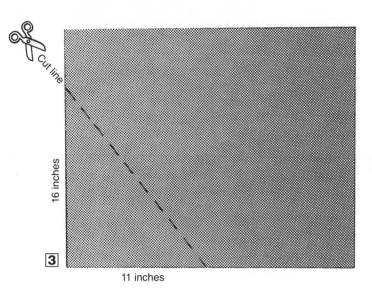

A sheet of newspaper

16 inches

11 inches

Cut line

3

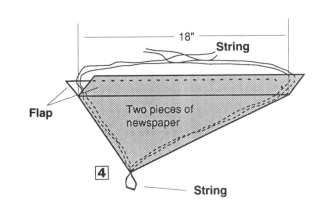

18"

String

Flap

Two pieces of
newspaper

String

4

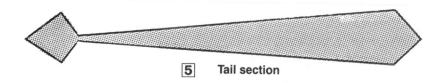

5   **Tail section**

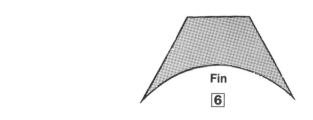

Fin

6

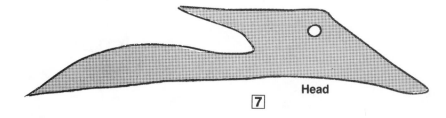

Head

7

String, Tail, and Head

4. Draw a triangle in a corner of a piece of newspaper. The two sides of the triangle that run along the corner will measure 16 inches and 11 inches (40 cm and 28 cm). See 3.

5. Repeat step 4 so that you have two triangles. Fold a 2-inch flap on each triangle.

6. Cut a length of string at 100 inches (approx. 2.5 m), cut it in half, and place the two lengths along the inside edges of the short sides of one of the triangles. Make a loop that extends outside the triangle's point and let the long string ends extend from the triangle's 18-inch side. (See 4.) Brush diluted glue over the triangle and strings (not on the flaps), and place the second triangle on top. Pat the paper together and let it dry.

7. Cut out the tail shape 5 from *two* sheets of newspaper. The tail should measure about 28 inches (70 cm) long. Cut another length of string, double it, place in the center of the newspaper sheets, and let the string ends extend beyond the part of the tail that attaches to the body. Glue the sheets together and set the tail aside to dry.

8. Make a fin 6 and head 7 as shown here and cut them out of stiff paper.

Putting It Together

9. Poke two holes in the kite, about 18 inches apart, along the wire that runs down the kite's center. (See **8**.) Position the triangle with the looped string onto the underside of the kite with flaps spread out. The short side of the triangle should be toward the "head" of the kite. Thread the string ends through the holes you made in the kite. Tie the string ends together in one strong knot.

10. Be sure the triangle lies snugly against the kite. Glue the flaps flat against the kite. Trim off the excess string. Tape over the knot for extra support. (The loop of string that points down from the kite is used to tie your ball of string for flight control.)

11. Place the tail on the kite and tie the tail string to the string on top of the kite. Glue the tail to the kite and let it dry.

12. Tear strips of newspaper, dip them in diluted glue, and place the strips along each side of the "neck" to attach the head. Place strips over the string on top of the kite. (See **9**.)

13. Use scissors to cut a slit for the fin to fit into the end of the tail. (See **10**.) Dip strips of paper in glue and place the strips on both sides of the fin to attach it.

14. Once the glue has dried completely, your *Pterosaur* is ready to soar!

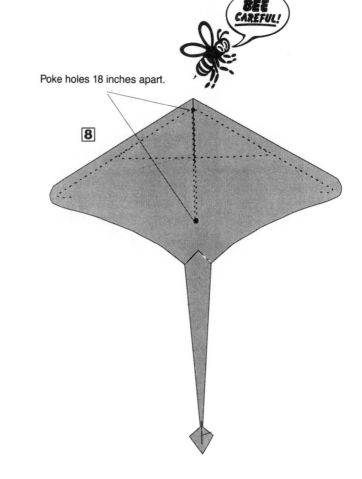

Poke holes 18 inches apart.

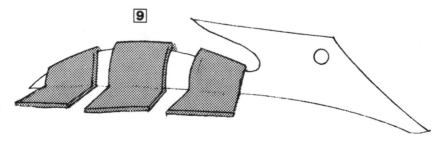

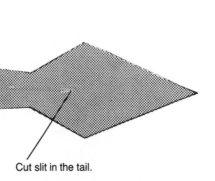

Cut slit in the tail.

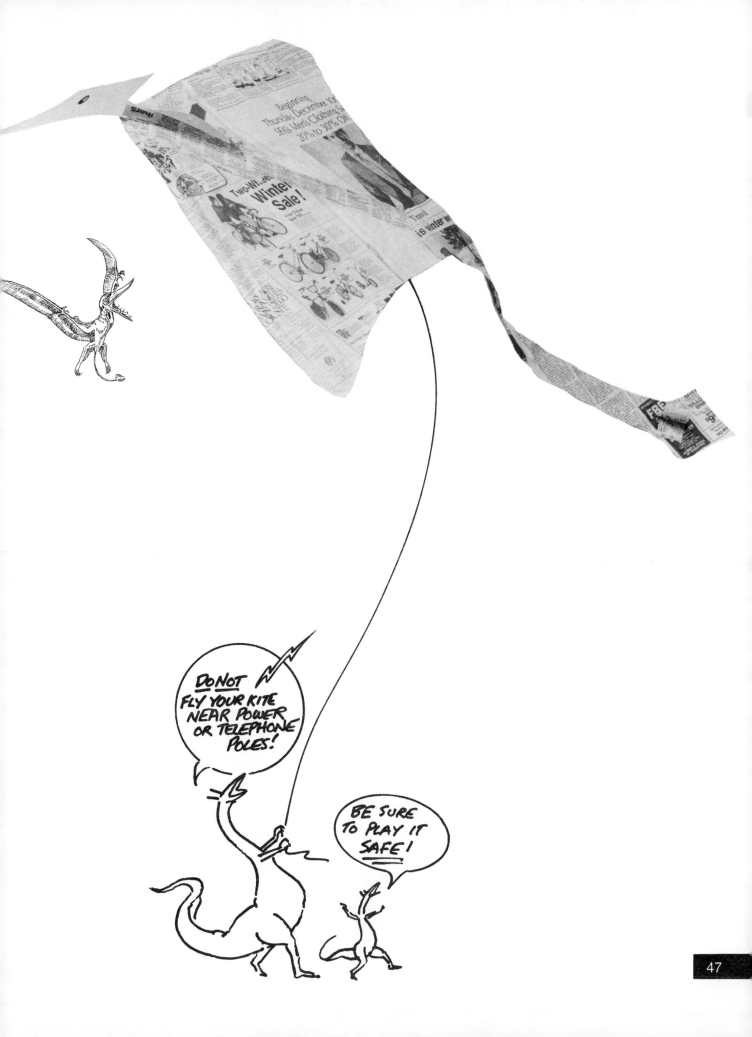

Ruling the Skies!

A Key Word Puzzle

Some animals started to fly because there were great advantages in being in the sky. There were places that other animals could not reach. There were new sources of food. The sky was safer than the ground.

For each definition below **fill in the blanks** with the word that is described. Then put together the circled letters to write a word telling about the animals that ruled the skies.

1. The force that pushes a wing up into the air. The shape of a wing causes it to have this.

2. Tiny rods that are hooked together to make feathers that are strong but light in weight.

3. An early bird that looks like it was part dinosaur and part bird. Seems to show that birds are dinosaurs.

   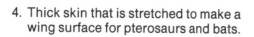

4. Thick skin that is stretched to make a wing surface for pterosaurs and bats.

   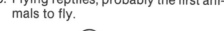

5. Flying reptiles, probably the first animals to fly.

6. Small rods of bone inside the hollow bones of birds. These prop up the walls of the bones to make them stronger.

   — — — — —

Use the circled letters to answer this question.

Who ruled the skies?

— — — — — — —

BEE CAREFUL!

Tape

1 Tape 3 straight-ened coathangers together. Be sure to bend over tips and wrap with tape.

2 Wrap lots of newspaper around straight/taped coat-hangers. Make a cone shape as shown at right.

3

4

5

A Giant Feather

Make it simple or make it complex. You can make it as big as you wish—even as long as a car!

The largest bird that ever lived had some feathers that were more than **3 feet long** (1 meter). Although these giant feathers probably weighed less than an ounce (30 grams), they were very strong.

You can make a giant prehistoric feather. You'll need: newspaper, tape white glue mixed with equal parts of water, and scissors

The Shaft

1. Ask an adult to straighten three coathangers and break off the coiled and hooked ends. The adult then can wrap the tips with tape. You can place two hangers end to end. Center the third hanger over the two, making one long shaft that is strong in the middle. Tape the hangers together. **1**

BEE CAREFUL!

2. Wrap many sheets of newspaper around the coathangers. Make a cone shape **2**. Roll the cone tightly. Tape it. Fold over the open end, taping it closed.

The Vanes

3. Open two sheets of newspaper. Place one above the other so they overlap slightly **3**. Glue together the two sheets where they overlap. Then spread glue all over the two sheets. Place two more sheets of newspaper on top of them. Repeat this step with four other sheets of newspaper. You'll now have two sets of layered newspaper.

4. Cover the first set of layered newspapers with glue. Place the shaft on top of it, letting the thick end of the shaft extend beyond the newspaper **4**. Quickly, spread glue over the shaft. Place the other set of layered newspapers over the shaft and the first set of newspapers. The shaft is now glued between the two sets of layered newspaper.

5. After the glue has dried, use a marker or pencil to draw the outline of a feather **5**. Paint your feather, then cut it out. Finally, draw upward pointing lines from the shaft to the edge of the feather with pencil. Then cut along the lines to make the vanes.

49

Sweet-Tooth Tigers

USE ALMONDS ALONG THE BACK

CANDY KISSES MAKE SWEET EYES!

COCONUT CLAWS

GUMDROPS MAKE BIG TEETH!

These cookies will make even a cranky Smilodon smile.

Make the dough, then shape it into mammals or monsters. Frost your creations once they have baked. Then decorate them with gumdrops, candies, chocolate chips, caramels, miniature marshmallows, or coconut.

Dough:

1 egg

1½ cups (350 g) sifted flour

½ cup (100 g) sugar

¼ cup (50 g) butter or margarine (½ stick)

¼ teaspoon (1 ml) vanilla extract (optional)

BEE CAREFUL!

1. Blend butter and sugar together just until creamy. Beat the egg. Add it and the vanilla to the butter and sugar. Add the flour and knead it into a dough. Press into a ball, wrap in plastic wrap, and chill at least two hours.

2. Preheat oven to 400°F (200°C). Grease a baking sheet. Pull pieces from the dough to make shapes. Put the creatures on the baking sheet. Bake 8 minutes if the dough is thin. For thick creatures, bake 10 minutes or more. Wear protective oven mitts.

3. Let cookies cool on a wire rack. Decorate with frosting.

Frosting:

Put sifted powered sugar in a bowl and beat in enough lemon juice and water until the mixture is thin enough to spread.

Eat 'em up!

Mammals!

ACROSS

1. Special cheek teeth that some meat-eating mammals have. Used to cut up meat before it is swallowed. (two words)
3. Places held in a community of animals by different kinds of animals. These are often filled by other animals when a species dies out.
4. Many meat-eaters evolved these on the ends of their feet for grabbing and holding prey.
6. Plant-eating mammals that eat mostly leaves and other parts of bushes and trees.
7. Something that mammals can make inside their own bodies and that their hair keeps in.
8. Plant-eating mammals that eat mostly grass. They have very large cheek teeth for grinding up their tough food.
9. Any animal belonging to the group of warm-blooded animals with specialized teeth.
10. Change over time. New things do this from older things.
11. Ancient marine reptiles that died out when the dinosaurs became extinct. One of the reptiles that left niches that were filled by sea mammals.

DOWN

1. Long, sharp teeth that meat-eating mammals use for grabbing and holding their prey.
2. Small teeth in front of the mouth that are used to cut food. Meat-eating mammals use them to get bits of meat off bones.
5. Any animal that eats other animals.

51

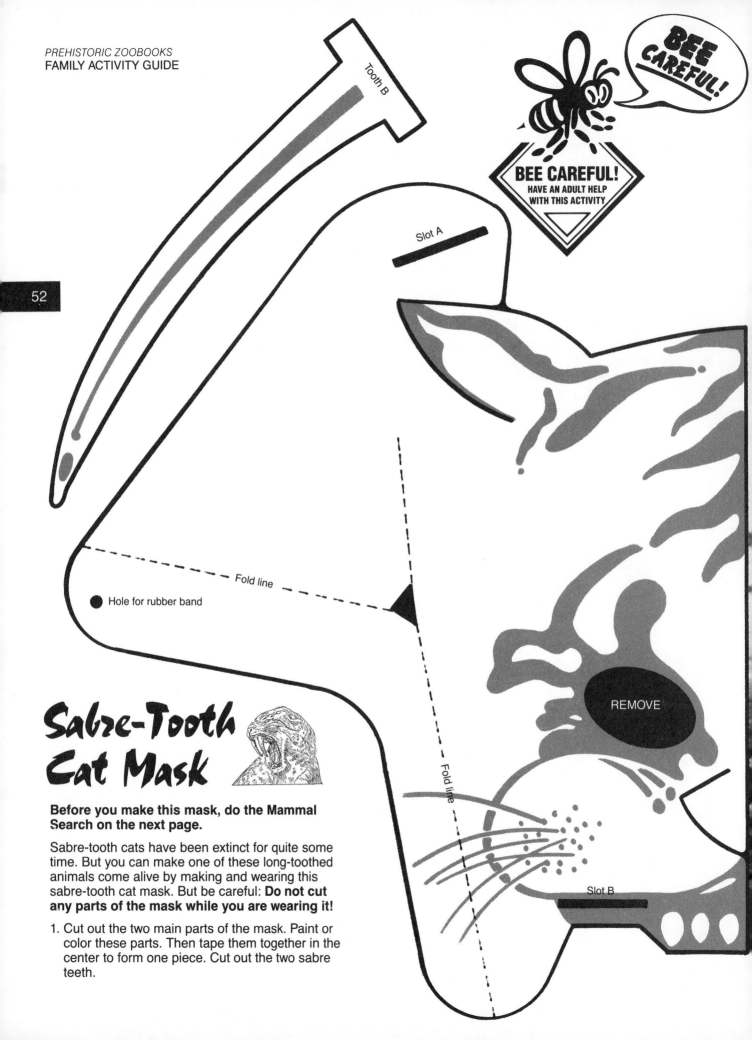

Tooth B

BEE CAREFUL!

BEE CAREFUL!
HAVE AN ADULT HELP
WITH THIS ACTIVITY

Slot A

52

Fold line

● Hole for rubber band

REMOVE

Fold line

Slot B

Sabre-Tooth Cat Mask

Before you make this mask, do the Mammal Search on the next page.

Sabre-tooth cats have been extinct for quite some time. But you can make one of these long-toothed animals come alive by making and wearing this sabre-tooth cat mask. But be careful: **Do not cut any parts of the mask while you are wearing it!**

1. Cut out the two main parts of the mask. Paint or color these parts. Then tape them together in the center to form one piece. Cut out the two sabre teeth.

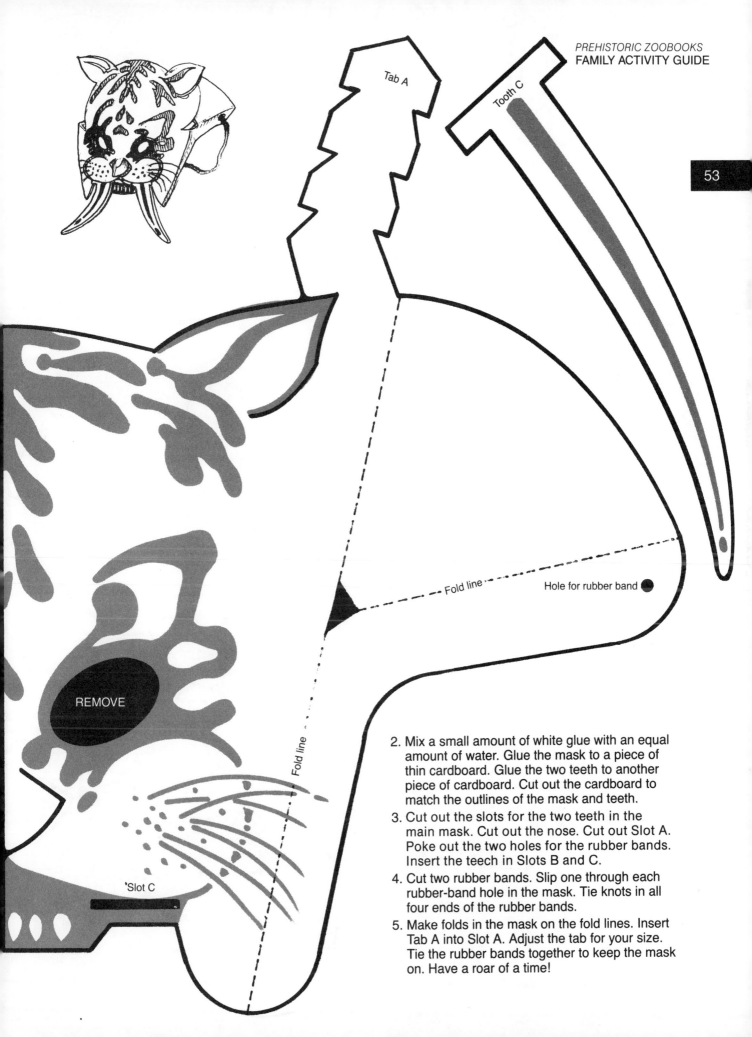

Tab A

Tooth C

Fold line · · · · Hole for rubber band

REMOVE

Fold line

Slot C

2. Mix a small amount of white glue with an equal amount of water. Glue the mask to a piece of thin cardboard. Glue the two teeth to another piece of cardboard. Cut out the cardboard to match the outlines of the mask and teeth.

3. Cut out the slots for the two teeth in the main mask. Cut out the nose. Cut out Slot A. Poke out the two holes for the rubber bands. Insert the teech in Slots B and C.

4. Cut two rubber bands. Slip one through each rubber-band hole in the mask. Tie knots in all four ends of the rubber bands.

5. Make folds in the mask on the fold lines. Insert Tab A into Slot A. Adjust the tab for your size. Tie the rubber bands together to keep the mask on. Have a roar of a time!

Mammal search

The dead dinosaur is easy to find in this picture. See it? After the dinosaurs were long gone, mammals populated the earth. Mammals adapted to the lands where they lived. Big or small, spotted, striped, fast or slow, mammals have survived. They have evolved into many amazing species.

Several mammals are hidden in this picture. Look inside and all around the dinosaur. Look for the lion, beaver, rhinoceros, and porcupine. Find the back of a zebra. There's a whale, too.
The hidden animals are different sizes. How many can you find?

Artiodactyls— or an ARTful Set of Horns

Artiodactyls developed a greater variety of horns than any other mammals. Although these ARTy horns were developed for protection, they were often quite beautiful. You can horn in on this beauty by making your own set of artiodactyl horns to wear. Cut out or trace the headband and horns on these two pages. Color your horns decoratively with crayons or felt pens. Or, paint a design. Just be ARTistic.

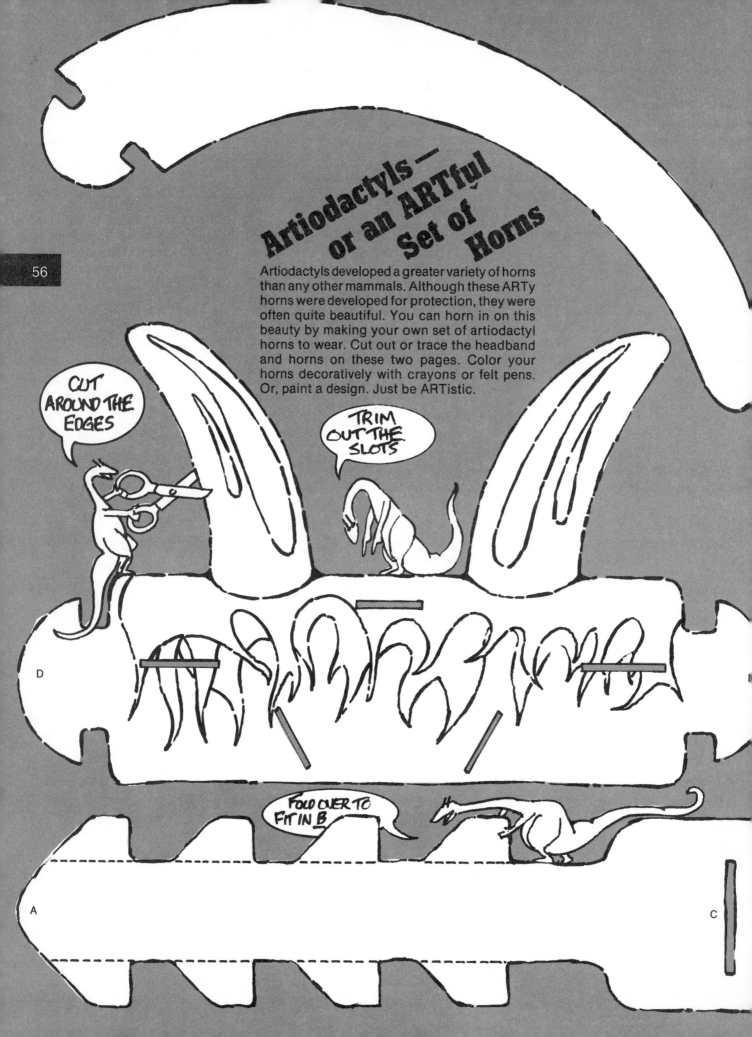

(Trace and lengthen these sections for larger head sizes.)

MAMMAL CONSTRUCTION

You can make some **herbivore mammals** out of some of the foods they might eat.

Here's a list of foods and materials you might use. Ask permission before you raid the kitchen. Ask an adult to help you slice fruits or vegetables.

Use a potato, squash, apple, or orange as the main body part. Add wings, feet, armor, spikes, eyes, a nose, and a tail—or more.

See how many different mammals you can come up with. Have a contest with your friends. Make a "scene" with many different herbivores interacting. Perform a play with your creatures as the actors!

Here are some foods to use as parts.

macaroni   dried beans   nuts   pumpkin seeds   melon seeds

whole cloves   gumdrops   caramels   licorice   marshmallows
pretzel sticks   dried fruit   raisins   pea pods   carrot slices
celery stalks   apples   oranges   lemons   cauliflower   broccoli
squash   radishes   potatoes

You might use these, too.

toothpicks   ice cream sticks   pipe cleaners
straws, cut into pieces   yarn   cotton balls

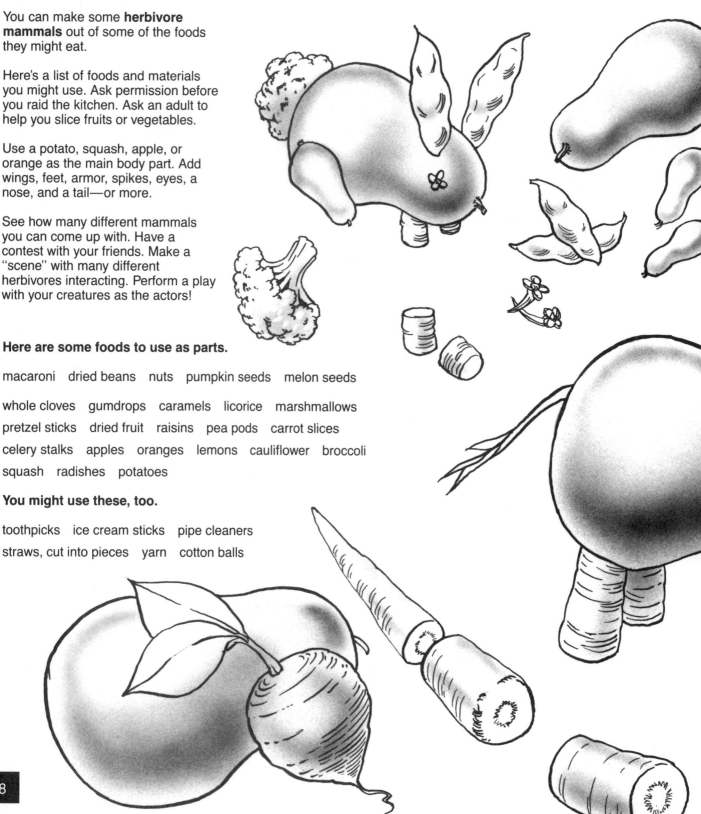

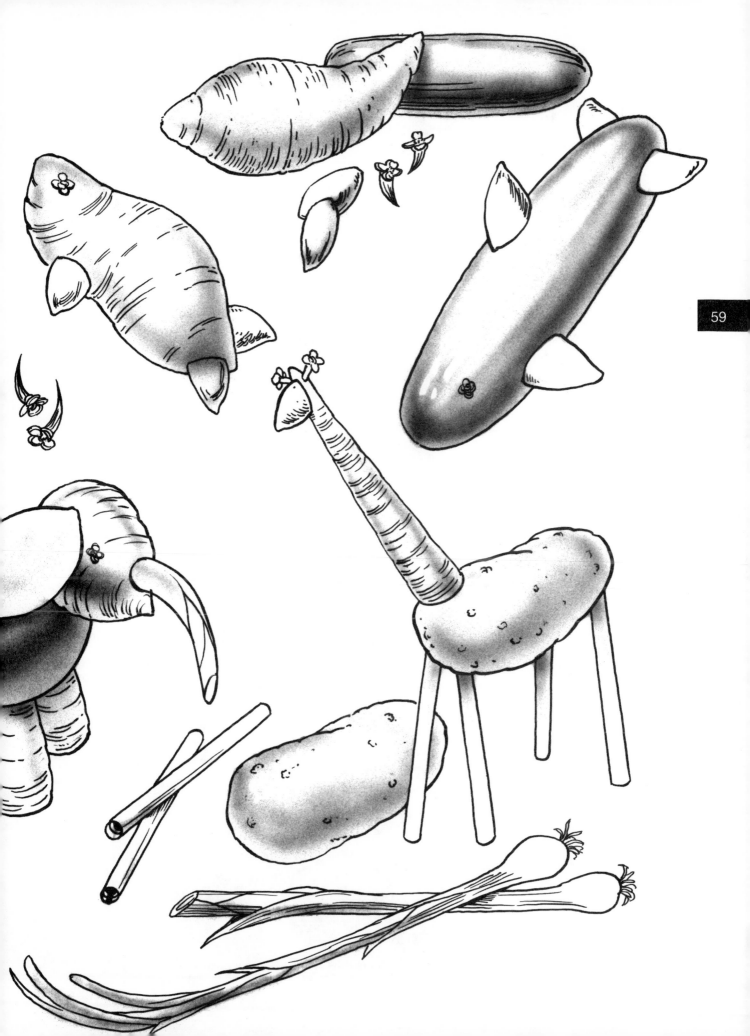

Scrambled

With the dinosaurs gone, the tiny mammals were free to move into many empty niches. They radiated and evolved into a wonderful array of different animals. **Unscramble the words in capital letters** so you can read about this wonderful variety of mammals.

1. The variety of **TLANP-INGATE** animals was astonishing.

2. Some grew very large, like the **THESLAPEN.** Their size protected them from **STARPODER.**

3. Many large plant-eaters developed **KUSTS** and **STRUNK** to help them get food.

4. Other plant-eaters stayed small, like the **STRODEN,** so they could hide in small places where their predators could not reach.

5. **STRODEN** had **THETE** that could eat almost anything, so they survived when food was scarce.

6. Some plant-eaters developed **RROAM,** so they could defend themselves.

7. Hoofed mammals are called **GLUETANUS** and often grew to large size.

8. Many hoofed animals had large **SROHN** on their heads for **CRITTONOPE.**

9. Today, there are two different kinds of ungulates, and you can tell them apart by **TONGUNIC** their **STEO.**

10. Perissodactyls have an **DOD BUNMER** of **STEO.** Artiodactyls have an **NEEV BUNMER** of **STEO.**

11. Artiodactyls are famous for their great variety of **SROHN** and **SNARELT.**

12. Some artiodactyls called **MANRUNITS** have special teeth and four **CHOTMASS** for eating grass.

13. Some mammals called **RAPTIMES** found food and protection up in the **EREST.**

14. To help them jump from tree to tree, they developed excellent eyes and the first **BHMSTU.**

15. To control their wonderful eyes and hands, **RAPTIMES** needed larger **SANRIB.** They became more **ITENLEGLINT.**

Family Activities
Answer Key!

Pages 2 and 3: Be a Detective

Mystery	Cause (Who did it)	Proof
fish	cat	bones left near cat's bed and food dish
strawberries	girl	tennis-shoe tracks and fingerprints
cupcake	raccoon	raccoon tracks
sunflower seeds	bird	bird tracks and seeds near nest
cookies	dog	cookies near doggie door
popcorn	mouse	kernels near mouse hole

Page 5: What's the Word for . . . ?

Hypothesis — An attempt to explain how something works.

Experiment — A test to see if a hypothesis really explains something.

Scientific theory — Many facts and ideas gathered together to try to explain how some part of the world works (2 words).

Atoms — The very, very small pieces that everything is made of.

Particles — The even smaller pieces that atoms are made of.

Nucleus — The group of particles that forms the center of an atom.

Electrons — The particles that move around the nucleus.

Molecules — Groups of atoms joined together.

Page 9: Hard Facts

Make these matches between the clues and answers to progress through the maze:

OLDEST LIVING THINGS — simple
NEW LIVING THINGS DO THIS FROM OLD — evolve
ROCK LAYERS — sediments
BIG CHANGE — mutation
BREAK DOWN ROCKS — erode
LIVING THINGS HAVE BEEN ON EARTH — 3½ billion years
STONE ANIMALS — fossils
ATOMS DO THIS OVER TIME — change
MOST ROCKS ARE MADE OF — lava
PROCESS OF CHANGE OVER MILLIONS OF YEARS — evolution

Pages 22 and 23: A Fish Story

Some kinds of invertebrates evolved into **vertebrates**. Tunicates had free-swimming **larvae**. The larvae of tunicates had **notochords**. The notochords were **primitive backbones** (two words). After a time, notochords evolved into real backbones. And the larvae evolved into **primitive fish** (two words).

Life was dangerous for the first fish. As a result, many fish evolved hard **armor** to protect them. The armor was made of **bone**. Early fish had **small mouths** (two words), so they could only eat small food. But some armored fish evolved **jaws**. With better jaws to catch more food, some armored fish grew very big, like the giant **Dunkleosteus**.

Sharks evolved streamlined bodies with less armor. They could swim better than armored fish. Sharks also "invented" the first real **teeth**. But **bony fishes** (two words) were the best swimmers. They were also the first animals to have **lungs**. Bony fish also had the first **skeletons** made of strong bone. Strong skeletons and lungs made it possible for **lobe-finned fishes** (three words) to crawl out of the water.

Page 26: Breathing Easy

Page 27: Out of Water

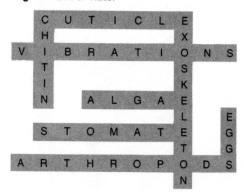

Pages 30 and 31: Break the Code!

1. **Metabolize:** To burn food and change it into energy.

2. **Digesting:** How a body uses chemical reactions to turn food into energy.

3. **Pelycosaurs:** A group of early reptiles that grew larger and larger.

4. **Dimetrodon:** A large meat-eating pelycosaur with a sail on its back.

5. **Therapsids:** Group of reptiles that may have been the first warmblooded animals on earth. Ancestors of the mammals.

6. **Thecodonts:** The ancestors of the dinosaurs helped to cause the extinction of the therapsids.

7. **Nocturnal Animal:** An animal that is only active at night, staying hidden during the day to keep safe.

Page 40: Name That Dinosaur

Dinosaurs are listed clockwise from upper left:

1. Tyrannosaurus Rex
2. Ultrasaurus
3. Stegosaurus
4. Kronosaurus
5. Anklosaurus

Page 48: Ruling the Skies! — A Key Word Puzzle

1. lift
2. filaments
3. archaeopteryx
4. wing membrane
5. pterosaurs
6. struts

Key Word: **FLYERS**

Page 51: Mammals Crossword Puzzle

Pages 54 and 55: Mammal Search

There are 17 mammals hiding on these two pages. Clockwise: rhinoceros, lemur, lamb, lion, porcupine, zebra, chipmunk, bear, giraffe, elephant, kangaroo, whale, tapir, beaver, rabbit, sea lion, and dolphin.

Pages 60 and 61: Scrambled Mammals

1. The variety of **PLANT-EATING** animals was astonishing.

2. Some grew very large, like the **ELEPHANTS**. Their size protected them from **PREDATORS**.

3. Many large plant-eaters developed **TUSKS** and **TRUNKS** to help them get food.

4. Other plant-eaters stayed small, like the **RODENTS**, so they could hide in small places where their predators could not reach them.

5. **RODENTS** had **TEETH** that could eat almost anything, so they survived when food was scarce.

6. Some plant-eaters developed **ARMOR**, so they could defend themselves.

7. Hoofed mammals are called **UNGULATES** and often grew to large size.

8. Many hoofed animals had large **HORNS** on their heads for **PROTECTION**.

9. Today, there are two different kinds of ungulates, and you can tell them apart by **COUNTING** their **TOES**.

10. Perissodactyls have an **ODD NUMBER** of **TOES**. Artiodactyls have an **EVEN NUMBER of TOES**.

11. Artiodactyls are famous for their great variety of **HORNS** and **ANTLERS**.

12. Some artiodactyls called RUMINANTS have special teeth and four **STOMACHS** for eating grass.

13. Some mammals called **PRIMATES** found food and protection up in the **TREES**.

14. To help them jump from tree to tree, they developed excellent eyes and the first **THUMBS**.

17. To control their wonderful eyes and hands, **PRIMATES** needed larger **BRAINS**. They became more **INTELLIGENT**.

Lambeosaurus

Saichania

Saurolophus

Estemmenosuchus

Styracosaurus

Parasaurolophus

Ouranosaurus

Ceratosaurus

Stegosaurus

Saurolophus
(sore-OL-uh-fuss)

Lived about 70 to 75 million years ago

Up to 40 feet long

A rather large plant-eating dinosaur with **a special nose**. The bones in the nose were stretched out, and they may have been used **for making noise**. Some scientists believe there was a hollow air sack attached to the nose. When air was pushed out of the sack and through the nose, it might have made **a honking sound**. In this way, the dinosaurs may have "talked" to each other.

Saichania
(sigh-CHAIN-ee-uh)

Lived about 70 to 75 million years ago

Up to 25 feet long

An armored dinosaur with heavy armor all over its body. Saichania had very strong jaws and a strong mouth — and this shows that it probably ate **very tough food**. The armor on its huge head was made of thick lumps of bone, and the body was protected with spikes and plates. When it was attacked by predators, Saichania probably hid under all this armor like a huge turtle under a shell.

Lambeosaurus
(LAMB-bee-uh-saw-rus)

Lived about 75 million years ago

Up to 56 feet long

This duck-billed dinosaur had unusual **bony growths** on its head. There was a hollow crest pointing toward the front of the head, and a solid bony spike pointing toward the rear. Lambeosaurus was a plant-eater, with a special bill in front of its mouth for chopping off plants.

Parasaurolophus
(para-sore-OL-uh-fuss)

Lived about 75 million years ago

Up to 33 feet long

The crest on this duck-billed dinosaur was spectacular! Sprouting from the top of its head, the crest arched back **more than 6 feet**. It was hollow inside and connected to the dinosaur's nose — and some scientists believe that it could have been used **to make sounds**. Like a trumpet, the huge crest might have magnified sounds so the dinosaurs could signal to each other over long distances.

Styracosaurus
(stih-RAK-uh-saw-rus)

Lived about 75 million years ago

Up to 20 feet long

This horned dinosaur had horns on its face, and a bony frill over its neck, like most members of the group. But the frill of Styracosaurus was really something special. Along the edge, there were **very large spikes**. The spikes on males were probably used to attract females — like the big feathers of peacocks are used today. Like rhinos, horned dinosaurs probably used the horns on their noses to protect themselves.

Estemmenosuchus
(est-uh-men-o-SUE-cuss)

Lived about 245 million years ago

About 20 feet long

This early reptile was large like a dinosaur and it had strange horns on its head like some dinosaurs. But it lived a long time before the first true dinosaurs appeared on earth. It was probably a plant-eating animal — and its many horns were probably used to protect it from predators. The big teeth may have been used for the same purpose.

Stegosaurus
(STEG-uh-saw-rus)

Lived about 155 million years ago

Up to 30 feet long

The row of plates on the back of this plant-eating dinosaur has puzzled scientists for years. Some say the plates were a kind of armor for defense. Others say they were used to cool the dinosaurs off by cooling their blood. But everybody agrees that the spikes on the tail of Stegosaurus were used to chase away predators. This dinosaur had weak jaws and teeth, so it probably could eat only soft plants.

Ceratosaurus
(ser-AT-uh-saw-rus)

Lived about 145 to 155 million years ago

Up to 30 feet long

The name means "horned lizard," and the big horn on the nose of this dinosaur is easy to see. But nobody really knows what is was used for. It may have been used **as a weapon** — or it may have been used like the horns of some modern animals **in fights between males**. These dinosaurs were meat-eaters, with huge jaws that could open very wide, and many sharp teeth. They may have lived and hunted in packs like wolves.

Ouranosaurus
(oo-RAN-uh-saw-rus)

Lived about 130 to 140 million years ago

Up to 23 feet long

A strange plant-eating dinosaur from Africa that probably had a "sail" on its back. In the place that it lived, the climate was hot — and some scientists believe that the sail was used to **cool off** Ouranosaurus. There could have been many blood vessels in the sail. Blood that flowed through the sail could be cooled more easily by the air. And the cooler blood would cool the body.

Protoceratops

Iguanodon

Coelophysis

Camarasaurus

Tarbosaurus

Ohmdenosaurus

Euoplocephalus

Mamenchisaurus

Triceratops

Coelophysis
(seal-oh-FY-sis)
Lived about 200 million years ago
Up to 10 feet long

This early meat-eating dinosaur was probably a fierce hunter. It had long legs for running fast after prey. And it had "hands" with three fingers and claws that could grab and hold on to prey. It also had many sharp teeth, with serrated edges for cutting meat. Coelophysis was **very light** for its size. One of these dinosaurs that was 10 feet long probably weighed **less than 50 pounds**! These rather small dinosaurs probably lived and hunted in groups.

Iguanodon
(ee-GWAN-uh-don)
Lived about 130 to 140 million years ago
Up to 30 feet long

This plant-eating dinosaur lived in herds, like antelope do today. It spent most of its time quietly eating ferns and other plants near rivers and streams. Iguanodon could probably **run very fast** to escape from predators. It had long rear legs that could take large steps — and it could rear up and run on these long legs when it wanted to increase its speed. There was **a large spike** on each front foot, and the spikes were probably used as weapons.

Protoceratops
(pro-toe-SER-uh-tops)
Lived about 75 to 80 million years ago
Up to 9 feet long

An early horned dinosaur. It did not actually have horns on its face, like later members of the group. But it had **a broad frill** of bone at the back of its head, like later horned dinosaurs. And like the later members of the group, it had **a beak** that was used for chopping plants. The first dinosaur eggs ever discovered were Protoceratops eggs. This small dinosaur lived in Asia, in an area that is now Mongolia.

Ohmdenosaurus
(om-DAY-nuh-saw-rus)
Up to 25 feet long

This sauropod was one of the smaller members of the group — but it was still a big animal. Like all sauropods, it had a long neck and a long tail. Its body was heavy, and it needed strong legs to hold it up. When it moved, it probably moved rather slowly. Ohmdenosaurus used its long neck to reach up into trees for food, and it took in huge amounts of leaves every day.

Tarbosaurus
(TAR-bow-saw-rus)
Lived about 65 to 70 million years ago
Up to 46 feet long

This huge meat-eating dinosaur was a close relative of Tyrannosaurus rex — and looked like Tyrannosaurus in many ways. It had the same kind of enormous jaws, with many serrated teeth. It ran on two feet, and had a long tail to balance its body. And its favorite prey were probably plant-eating dinosaurs, including duck-billed and armored dinosaurs. When it could not catch prey, it may have eaten animals killed by other predators.

Camarasaurus
(kuh-MARE-uh-saw-rus)
Lived about 155 million years ago
Up to 59 feet long

A sauropod dinosaur with a long neck and a long tail. The long neck helped it to reach up into trees for food. It had teeth that were shaped like spoons, and probably used them to cut off tough plants. Camarasaurus had **enormous nose openings** on top of its head, and nobody is sure why they were so big. Some scientists say that it may have had a trunk like an elephant for grabbing tree branches.

Triceratops
(tri-SER-uh-tops)
Lived about 65 million years ago
Up to 35 feet long

The name means "three-horned face," and that is a very good description. There were two long horns above the eyes, and a smaller horn over the nose. The strong beak was used for cutting plants, and also for biting predators. Like all horned dinosaurs, Triceratops had a large frill over its neck. These dinosaurs probably lived in groups, like White Rhinos do today. And they probably behaved like rhinos as well.

Mamenchisaurus
(ma-MENSH-uh-saw-rus)
Lived about 155 million years ago
Up to 72 feet long

A very large sauropod with **the longest neck** of any known dinosaur. The neck was almost half of the entire length of the animal. Like many other sauropods, Mamenchisaurus used its neck to reach up into trees for food. But the extra length of its neck gave it **a special advantage**. It could probably reach into the highest parts of the tallest trees — and eat leaves that no other dinosaurs could reach.

Euoplocephalus
(you-oh-plo-SEF-uh-lus)
Lived about 70 to 75 million years ago
Up to 18 feet long

An armored dinosaur with elaborate armor to protect it from predators. There were bands of armor running down its back, and there were huge chunks of bone on the back as well. Thick plates of bone covered its neck, and triangle-shaped spines protected the shoulders. The head of Euoplocephalus was wrapped in armor — and **even the eyelids had armor**! This dinosaur was a plant-eater, with a strong beak for cutting plants.